Guide to Initial Periodic Inspection and Testing of Electrical Installations

National Association of Professional Inspectors and Testers

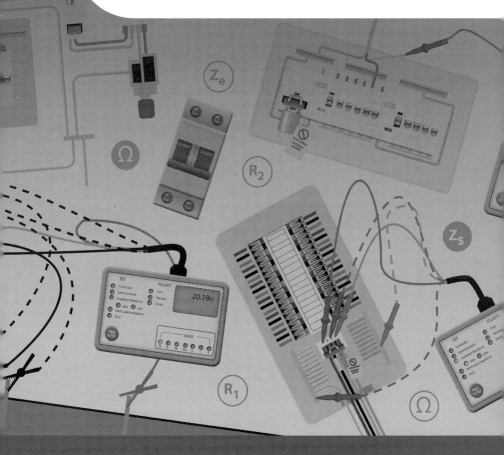

Complies with BS 7671:2018+A1 (2020)

NAPIT

First published by NAPIT Publishing Limited 2021

NAPIT Publishing is part of the NAPIT Group of Companies
Copyright© 2021, NAPIT Publishing Limited

NAPIT Publishing Limited
Registered Office:
The Gardeners Lodge,
The Business Park,
Pleasley Vale,
Mansfield,
Nottinghamshire,
NG19 8RL
Email: info@napit.org.uk
www.napit.org.uk

ISBN Number: 978-1-8382214-0-9 (print)
ISBN Number: 978-1-8382214-1-6 (electronic)

Note:
Every possible effort has been made to ensure that the information contained within this book is accurate at the time of going to press and, the publishers and authors do not accept any responsibility for any errors or omissions however caused. No responsibility for loss or damages to any persons acting or otherwise as a result of the material within this publication can be accepted by the editor, the publisher or the authors.

British Library Cataloguing in Publication Data
A record for this book is available from the British Library.

Cooperating Organisations and Individuals

NAPIT Publishing would like to acknowledge, and thank, all the participating organisations, and individuals, who have given their advice, information and time, to enrich and enhance both the technical and operational aspects of this publication.

Cooperating Organisations

NAPIT Assurance

Hager

Megger

GAMBICA Association Ltd

Surge Protection Devices LTD

Prysmian Group

DEHN UK Limited

Cooperating Individuals

Richard Wardak MIET .... JPEL 64, 64 Sub A

Kirsty Johnson .... JPEL 64 Sub D (surge protection specialist)

Neil Hitchman BEng(Hons) IEng MCIBSE MIET .... JPEL 64 Sub A

Iain Collings ....JPEL 64 Sub B

Paul Collins IEng MIET .... JPEL 64 Sub A

Eur Ing Paul Sayer CEng FIET GCGI ....JPEL 64 Deputy Chair, JPEL 64 Sub A/B/C/D

Robin Earl .... JPEL 64 Sub D (surge protection specialist)

NAPIT Staff

Technical

Frank Bertie MIET...JPEL 64, 64 Sub A/C, IEC TC 64 MT4

Paul Chaffers MIET.. JPEL 64 Sub B Deputy Chair

Richard Townsend IEng CMS MIET......... JPEL 64 Sub C/D, IEC TC 64 MT1/MT2

Graphic Design and Production

Sean Coupe ....Graphic Design and illustration

Peter Gwyer, Utopia Design Solutions.. Typesetting

Authors

Richard Townsend IEng CMS MIET......... JPEL 64 Sub C/D, IEC TC 64 MT1/MT2

Paul Chaffers MIET.. JPEL 64 Sub B Deputy Chair

Editor

Richard Townsend IEng CMS MIET......... JPEL 64 Sub C/D, IEC TC 64 MT1/MT2

Contents

Preface

The National Association of Professional Inspectors and Testers (NAPIT) has long been the primary association for individuals and businesses, whose core business is the inspection and testing of electrical installations.

As we move towards an ever-legal requirement to ensure the safety of others, and especially the electrical installations that they use, NAPIT felt it was time to produce a definitive Guide to initial verification and periodic inspection and testing of electrical installations.

Building on its industry-leading portfolio of publications in this area and the strengths of its lead technical team, NAPIT has developed what we believe to be the most defining Guide for the electrical installation Inspector and Tester available today. NAPIT feel this new Guide will be invaluable for any electrician especially those looking to develop their existing skills.

Foreword

We believe that this new Guide will be a turning point for the information available to electrical installation Inspectors and Testers, especially those looking for a definitive point of reference during their everyday work.

It clearly establishes what is expected and what needs to be done to produce an effective and efficient Electrical Installation Certificate or Report.

As the leading Registration Electrical Inspector Scheme (EIS) for electrical Inspectors and Testers, we feel that there is no other publication available that provides the same level of hands on approach to guidance in this area.

Frank Bertie

NAPIT Chief Technical Officer

About the Authors

The two technical authors responsible for the production of NAPIT's Guide to Initial Verification and Periodic Inspection and Testing are:

Richard Townsend IEng CMS MIET
Paul Chaffers MIET

Richard Townsend IEng CMS MIET

Richard is the Principle Author responsible for the development of NAPIT's 'Landlords and Electrical Inspectors Guidance for the Private Rented Sector (PRS) Electrical Safety Checks' and also authored NAPIT's Code of Practice for Risk Assessment and Management.

Richard is also the author of the hugely successful and market leading NAPIT EICR Codebreakers, giving advice to Engineers, Clients, Landlords, Inspectors, and Duty Holders on Electrical Installation Condition Reports (EICRs), and how to understand them.

Prior to joining NAPIT, as the publisher and Principal Author, Richard was a senior IET engineer, responsible for maintaining BS 7671 and representing the IET at industry-leading events and government working groups. During his time there, Richard also authored the IET Code of Practice for In-service Inspection and Testing of Electrical Equipment (PAT) 4th Edition, which incorporated changes required by the Löfstedt report, to ensure businesses took a risk-based approach to compliance instead of using pre-set guidelines.

Richard now represents NAPIT on the JPEL 64 committees, which are the National committees responsible for developing the content of BS 7671. As well as national standards development, Richard is a member of two international Standards Committees, as a UK expert, developing worldwide safety standards.

Richard represented NAPIT on the post-Grenfell, Hackitt review working groups, to develop the changes in competencies and monitoring of workforces employed in HRB High-Rise Buildings.
Richard has a specialised engineering and facilities management background, starting life as a Naval Engineer, later owning and running a successful Contracting and FM business and prior to the IET and NAPIT, working for Serco Leisure, ensuring safe, efficient and cost-effective electrical practices were followed.

Paul Chaffers MIET

Paul started his career at NAPIT as Field Officer for the South-central region, before progressing to Regional Inspections Manager for London and the South East. Paul has been employed at NAPIT for over ten years and is now our Technical Events Manager, responsible for the technical intent of NAPIT exhibitions and seminars. He also represents NAPIT on numerous industry panels and is one of NAPITs leading presenters.

Paul represents NAPIT on the JPEL 64 committees, which are the National Committees responsible for developing the content of BS 7671, where he is the Deputy Chairman of Sub-committee B, which is responsible for thermal effects.

Before joining NAPIT, Paul ran a ship repair and electrical contracting company in Southampton. With over 30 years' experience, Paul has worked in many industries. Following the completion of his apprenticeship with the British Railways Board, Paul also has experience in Nuclear, Oil and Shipping Industries as well as various commercial environments such as data centres and dental practices.

Paul was the key author in the development of NAPIT's On-site Solutions, and co-authored NAPIT's 'Landlords and Electrical Inspectors Guidance for the Private Rented Sector (PRS) Electrical Safety Checks'.

Having authored numerous technical articles, and been published in several industry magazines, Paul has proven his expansive technical ability, where he utilises this wealth of knowledge, to complement the expertise of the NAPIT Publications Department.

Introduction

With the multitude of different types of wiring systems and installation methods currently in use, any Electrician or Inspector, carrying out initial verification or periodic inspection of an electrical installation, needs to have an understanding of what is available and how to deal with them.

Fully complying with the latest and most up to date Legislation and British Standards, this reference publication from NAPIT 'Guide to Initial Verification and Periodic Inspection and Testing of Electrical installations' aims to develop the skills needed to carry out initial verification and periodic inspection and testing.

It covers everything required from understanding different Earthing systems, Test equipment, to how to carry out the individual test required to comply with BS 7671.

The ongoing safety of existing installations and the importance of periodic inspection and testing is fully explained in the EICR in-depth Section, on how to produce an accurate and detailed Report.

Section 1
Legal Requirements

1.0 Health and Safety

1.1 The Health and Safety at Work Act etc. 1974 (HASWA)

This Act applies to all places of work except those workplaces which are covered by special Legislation, e.g., mines and quarries.

The Act places a duty on employers to ensure the safety of their employees and for employees to co-operate with their employers. In the case of self-employed persons, they would carry the responsibilities of both employer and employee. Also, there is a duty of care to ensure the safety of persons that are neither employers nor employees.

1.2 The Electricity at Work Regulations 1989 (EAWR)

These Regulations are enforced under the Health and Safety at Work Act.

The Regulations require that precautions must be taken against injury or death arising from electrical work with the emphasis on preventing danger from electric shock, burns, electrical explosion or arcing, or from fire or explosion initiated by electrical energy.

Guidance on the interpretation of the EAWR is provided in the Health and Safety Executive (HSE) Guidance on Regulations (HSR25).
The following is a short summary of the Regulations.

Regulation 4: Systems, work activities, and protective equipment
All electrical systems to be constructed and maintained so as to prevent 'so far as reasonably practicable,' danger. The condition of electrical systems is to be monitored throughout its life by inspection, and where necessary testing.

Regulation 5: Strength and capabilities of electrical equipment
No electrical equipment shall be put into use where its strength and capability may be exceeded in such a way as may give rise to danger. All equipment selected should meet appropriate standards, e.g., British Standards or similar International Standards, and installed in accordance with manufacturer's instructions, etc.

Regulation 6: Adverse or hazardous environments
All equipment shall be selected and installed to withstand exposure to mechanical damage, the effects of weather, natural hazards, temperature, and pressure.

Regulation 7: Insulation, protection and placing of conductors

All conductors shall be suitably covered with insulating material suitably placed and protected to prevent so far as reasonably practicable danger.

Regulation 8: Earthing and other suitable precautions

Any conductor other than a circuit conductor, which may become charged with electricity as a result of the use of or a fault occurring in the system, shall be installed to prevent the risk of electric shock.

Acceptable techniques include:

- Double insulated equipment
- Earthing
- Equipotential bonding
- Use of safe voltages
- Electrically separated or isolated systems

Regulation 9: Integrity of reference conductors

The integrity of referenced conductors connected to Earth shall be maintained, no fuse, circuit-breaker or switch shall be inserted in the conductor.

Regulation 10: Connections

Any joint or connection in a system shall be mechanically and electrically suitable for use.

Regulation 11: Means of protecting from excess current

A means of protection should be provided at the origin of each circuit and at points in a circuit where a reduction in cable size takes place. The means of protection is usually a fuse or circuit-breaker.

Regulation 12: Means for cutting off the supply and for isolation

In order to prevent danger, a suitable means shall be provided for

- Cutting off the supply of electrical energy to electrical equipment
- Isolation of electrical equipment

Suitable devices for cutting off the supply are switches capable of being operated under normal and fault conditions.

Suitable devices for isolation are devices that have an adequate air gap between contacts, which should be externally visible or reliably indicated. A plug and socket-outlet and a double-pole switch are likely suitable devices.

Regulation 13: Precautions for work on equipment made dead
Adequate precautions shall be taken to prevent electrical equipment, which has been made dead from becoming electrically charged.

The procedure to be used usually involves:
- Identifying the installation/circuit
- Operating the isolating device
- Selecting a suitable voltage indicator
- Proving the correct operation of the voltage indicator immediately before and after testing the isolation of the installation/circuit

Regulation 14: Work on or near live conductors
No person shall be engaged in any work activity on or near any live conductors so as to prevent danger unless:
- It is unreasonable for it to be dead, and
- It is reasonable in all circumstances for him/her to be at work on or near it while it is live, and
- Suitable precautions are taken to prevent injury

Regulation 15: Working space access and lighting
Adequate working space and lighting shall be provided at all electrical equipment, where work is being carried out in circumstances that may give rise to danger.

Regulation 16: Persons to be competent to prevent danger and injury
No person shall be engaged in any work activity where technical knowledge or experience is necessary to prevent danger or injury unless they possess such knowledge or experience.

Regulation 29: Defence
In any proceedings for an offence consisting of a contravention of Regulations 4(4), 5, 8, 9, 10, 11, 12, 13, 14, 15, 16 or 25, it shall be up to any person to prove that they took all reasonable steps and exercised all due diligence to avoid an offence under the Regulations.

1.3 The Construction (Design and Management) Regulations 2015

These statutory Regulations are enforced under the Health and Safety at Work Act. The purpose is to establish high standards in the management and control of construction and demolition work.

CDM 2015 came into force in Great Britain on 6th April 2015, replacing the 2007 CDM Regulations. They set out what people involved in construction work need to do to protect themselves from harm, including anyone the work affects, and for the first time, these Regulations are now also applicable to domestic installations.

CDM 2015 aims to improve health and safety in the industry by helping you to:

- Sensibly plan the work, so the risks involved are managed from start to finish
- Have the right people for the right job at the right time
- Co-operate and coordinate your work with others
- Have the right information about the risks and how they are being managed
- Communicate this information effectively to those who need to know
- Consult and engage with workers about the risks and how they are being managed

Electrical Inspectors should be aware that:

- All builders, whatever their size, will have to create a construction phase safety plan for all building projects
- All domestic projects will have to meet the same basic standards for the provision of welfare facilities as commercial projects
- Any domestic projects where there has been more than one contractor must have a Health and Safety file presented at the end
- There is a Health and Safety file/handover pack available, which should include 'as-built' drawings or specifications of components that have been installed. Conveyancing solicitors are likely to request this when a property is bought and sold
- For homeowners, CDM duties are passed to the contractor where there is only one, or to the principal contractor for more than one

- Where there is more than one contractor, a principal designer has been appointed, and they coordinate all matters relating to health and safety
- Where the principal designer changes or is not engaged to the end of a project, any responsibility for the file moves on and may rest finally with the principal contractor
- The principal contractor is responsible for operational site safety and passing information to the principal designer for the Health and Safety file
- Principal contractor to hand over the Health and Safety file/handover documentation to the Client on completion

1.4 The Electricity Safety, Quality and Continuity Regulations (ESQCR)

These Statutory Regulations are enforced under the EAWR. The Regulations impose requirements regarding the installation and use of electrical networks and equipment owned or operated by generators, distributors, transmitters of electrical energy meter operators and suppliers in providing electrical energy to consumers.

1.5 The Provision and Use of Work Equipment Regulations 1998 (PUWER)

All equipment and new work equipment, including everything hired or purchased second-hand, must comply with the Regulations.

Every employer must ensure that all work equipment is constructed or adapted to be suitable for the purpose for which it is intended.

Second-hand equipment must comply with the Regulations before being put into use.

Regulation 2
Gives a definition of work equipment, which means any tool or piece of equipment for use at work.

Regulation 4
Requires work equipment to be suitable for the purpose and only used under conditions for which it is suitable.

Regulation 5
Requires that work equipment is properly and adequately maintained.

Regulation 6

Deals with inspection and recording the fact that inspection has taken place.

Regulation 7, 8 and 9

Covers identified specific risks, information, and instructions to employees and the training of employees.

Regulation 10

Requires that purchased equipment has a CE mark stamped on it.

Note:

After the UK transition from the EU, we will also now need to take account of the UK CA stamp, which stands for UK Conformity Assessed. This is the new marking for goods placed for sale on the UK market. There will obviously be a transition period, where we will find both stamps being used. This does not mean, however, that historic CE stamps will render equipment carrying them obsolete.

Regulation 11 to 20

Contains all the provisions previously contained in the Factories Act and other Legislation covering machine guarding control systems and isolation.

Regulation 21

Deals with lighting, which must be suitable and sufficient, taking account of the work operation in progress. Employers may also have to consider the need for both access lighting and task lighting.

Regulation 22

Continues the subject of maintenance, by requiring all equipment to be constructed or adapted so that it is safe to maintain.

Regulation 23 and 24

Deals with 'markings' which must be clear and appropriate.

1.6 Personal Protective Equipment (PPE) 2002 and The Personal Protective Equipment at Work Regulations 1992

These Regulations set out principles for selecting, providing, maintaining, and using personal protective equipment (PPE).

PPE is defined as all equipment designed to be worn or held to protect against a risk to health and/or safety. This includes most types of protective clothing and equipment, for example, eye, foot, head protection, and high visibility clothing, with exceptions, for ordinary clothes and uniforms.

PPE should only be relied upon as a last resort and is provided free of charge by employers when employees are potentially placed at risk.
PPE is only suitable if it:

- Is appropriate for the risks and the working conditions
- Takes account of workers' needs and fits properly
- Gives adequate protection
- Is compatible with any other items of PPE worn

Employers PPE duties are to:

- Assess whether there are other ways of doing the job so that PPE is not necessary
- Assess the PPE is adequate for the particular risks and intended use to ensure it is suitable
- Provide High visibility clothing free of charge and replace if lost or damaged
- Give training, information, and instruction to employees on the use of PPE and how to look after it
- Ensure PPE is properly used
- Ensure PPE provided is properly maintained and cleaned

Employees duties are to:

- Use PPE as instructed by an employer for any given work task
- Notify damage of PPE to employer
- Notify employer of additional PPE requirements
- Take care of PPE to ensure continued satisfactory condition

A new initiative, being driven by the Electrical Safety Roundtable (ESR) – Electrical Safety in the Workplace, is aimed directly at Electricians, Electrical Inspectors, and their employers. It is generally taken that there are 5 points of standard PPE, for an individual:

1. Hard hats
2. Foot protection
3. High visibility clothing
4. Eye protection
5. Hearing protection

The new ESR initiative is classing Electricians lock-off kits as PPE. This initiative prescribes 6 points of PPE for an Electrician, or anyone needing to work on an electrical system of any kind:

1. Hard hats
2. Foot protection
3. High visibility clothing
4. Eye protection
5. Hearing Protection
6. Lock-off kit

Electrocution and serious shocks are still a large problem in the electrical industry. Employers and Inspectors alike need to be aware of the dangers and use safe isolation/lock-off kits when and wherever they work on electrical systems. It is irrelevant that these systems may have been energised in the past and are now shut down, they could be energised at any time.

A large portion of the testing work associated with carrying out EICRs may involve risk assessed live working, working on or isolating systems and circuits. It is for these reasons, Inspectors need to be fully aware of the dangers, the different methods of safe isolation and larger scale isolation monitoring protocols, as they may be required to operate them or be included within their remit, whilst on site.

1.7 Building Regulations

1.7.1 The Building Act 1984

Up to and including April 2010 amendments.
This Act imposed duties of various kinds on several groups or people from Local Authorities, Builders, Approved Inspectors and those intended to carry out building work.

1.7.2 The Building Regulations 2010 (England and Wales)

The Regulations are enforced under the Building Act and apply to England and Wales. Proper plans are required to be submitted, buildings are to be well constructed and energy efficient, and the spread of fire is to be resisted. The responsibility to make Building Regulations in Wales was transferred to Welsh ministers in December 2011, allowing new Building Regulations and guidance to be produced applicable to Wales only. However, at the time of printing this Inspection and Testing Guide, Wales continues to use Building Regulations 2010.

These Regulations are supported by separate documents containing practical and technical guidance on compliance with the Regulations, which are known as 'Approved Documents'. The approved documents which cover aspects of electrical installation work are:

- Part A Structure, for the depth of chases in walls
- Part B Fire Safety, covering the provision of Fire Alarm and Fire Detection Systems, fire resistance of holes through floors and walls
- Part C Site preparation and resistance to moisture of floors, walls, roofs, and ceilings
- Part E Resistance to the passage of sound for penetrations through floor and walls
- Part F Means of Ventilation, for adequate ventilation for people in buildings which include extractor fans
- Part L Conservation of Fuel and Power for energy-efficient lighting
- Part M Access to, and use of buildings, for the height of socket-outlets, switches, consumer units, etc.
- Part P Design and installation of electrical installations within dwellings, to protect persons operating, maintaining or altering installations from fire or injury

For the latest version of the Approved Documents, which are free downloads, refer to the online planning portal: https://www.planningportal.co.uk/info/200135/approved_documents for the UK, and https://gov.wales/building-regulations-approved-documents for the Welsh Building Regulations.

Purely from a BS 7671 inspection and testing perspective, we will only be dealing with the requirements of BS 7671, as this is the only way an Electrical Installation Condition Report (EICR) can be coded, or affect the outcome of a design or initial verification of an installation.

The following Building Regulations and requirements are for informational purposes and should not be used to alter the outcome of a BS 7671 EIC/EICR, unless they are expressly referred to in BS 7671.

Any deficiencies directly regarding Building Regulations will need to be addressed by the Client and may need further inspections carrying out to their respective Standards.

1.7.3 Approved Document A – Structure

The following requirements affect Electricians while carrying out electrical installation work connected with creating openings in walls and cutting chases into walls. It should be noted that Approved Document A applies to all work carried out, not just electrical.

Creating an opening in walls

No opening should be provided in walls below the ground floor except for small holes for services and ventilation etc., which should be limited to a maximum area of 0.1 m^3 and at not less than 2 m centres.

Chases

Vertical chases should not be deeper than one-third of the wall thickness or, in the case of cavity walls, one-third of the thickness of a leaf. Horizontal chases should not be deeper than one-sixth of the thickness of the wall or leaf. Chases should not be so positioned in a way that would impair the stability of the wall, particularly where hollow blocks are used, see Fig 1.1.

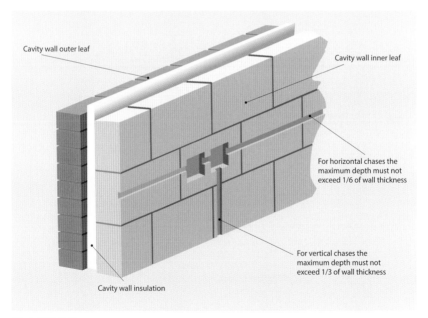

Fig 1.1 Wall Chases

1.7.4 Approved Document B Volume 1: Fire safety (Dwellings)

With around 12,000 electrical fires a year, Approved Document B is an important document for Electricians, especially designers. The Approved Document is divided into five separate requirements B1 to B5 as can be seen in Table 1.1.

Table 1.1 The 5 requirements of Approved document B	
B1	Means of warning and fire
B2	Internal fire spread (linings)
B3	Internal fire spread (structure)
B4	External fire spread
B5	Access and facilities for the fire service

The guidance in Approved Document B applies to all installation work carried out in new dwellings and applies only to existing installations in the following circumstance:

- Where a new habitable room is provided above ground level (e.g., extensions, loft conversions, etc.)
- Where holes are made in walls and ceilings to enable the installation of cables and pipes to pass-through
- Where a new habitable ground floor room with no external exit is provided

Requirement B1: means of warning and fire
Approved Document B provides guidance on fire alarm and early Detection Systems. This guidance is given by several clauses as can be seen here:

Clause 1.1: Requires that all dwellings should be provided with fire detection and alarm systems in accordance with the relevant parts of BS 5839-6 to at least a Grade D2 Category LD3 standard. Higher standards of protection are needed where occupants of a dwelling are subjected to a special risk of fire (consult BS 5839-6 for more information).

Clause 1.2: States that smoke alarms should be mains operated and conform to BS EN 14604 see Fig 1.2.

Fig 1.2 Mains powered alarm

Clause 1.3: States that heat alarms should be mains operated and conform to BS 5446-2.

Clause 1.4: Both smoke and heat alarms should have a standby power supply such as a battery or capacitor.

Recently BS 5839 Part 6 was amended to BS 5839-6:2019+A1:2020. The following is a short summary.

System grades

System Grades B and E were removed from the Standard, and Grades D and F were further split down, creating more grades of system types. This is summarised in Table 1.2.

Table 1.2 Grades of system	
Grade	**Definition**
Grade A	Separate detectors, sounders and central control and indicating equipment with back-up power supply
Grade C	A system of fire detectors and alarm sounders (which may be combined in the form of smoke alarms) connected to a common power supply with central control equipment
Grade D1	A system of one or more mains powered detectors, each with a tamper-proof standby supply consisting of a battery or batteries
Grade D2	A system of one or more mains powered detectors, each with an integral standby supply consisting of a user-replaceable battery or batteries
Grade F1	A system of one or more battery-powered detectors, powered by a tamper-proof primary battery or batteries
Grade F2	A system of one or more battery-powered detectors, powered by a user-replaceable primary battery or batteries

The Category of system

BS 5839 states that the level of protection to occupants needs to be directly related to the fire risk. Three Categories of systems are used to describe the level of protection each system provides; this is summarised in Table 1.3.

Table 1.3 System category		
System category	Level of protection	Position of detector/alarm
LD1	High	All areas where a fire could start e.g. hallways, landings, living rooms, kitchens, bedrooms, meter cupboards, loft conversions or lofts with equipment present such as an inverter
LD2	Medium	Escape routes and high-risk areas e.g. hallways, landings, kitchens and living rooms
LD3	Low	Escape routes e.g. hallways and landings

Note

Across all categories, alarms should not be installed within toilets, bathrooms or shower rooms.

In Scotland, under the Housing (Scotland) Act 1987 (Tolerable Standard) (Extension of Criteria) Order 2019, Grade F1 Category LD2 systems are required as a minimum in all existing dwellings by February 2021. This requirement applies to all homeowners and landlords.

Requirement B2: Internal fire spread (linings)

Electricians will need to comply with this requirement if they install luminaires with thermoplastic diffusers forming part of the ceiling, as illustrated in Fig 1.3. Where lay-in modular fittings require thermal and acoustic properties, for more specialised installations, fire hoods and similar products are available.

It is important that any thermal or fire barriers are not breached. Any devices or materials used must not reduce the fire integrity design of the original building fabric, or any subsequent modifications to it, which may include increased fire barriers due to change of use or change in Regulation or Legislation.

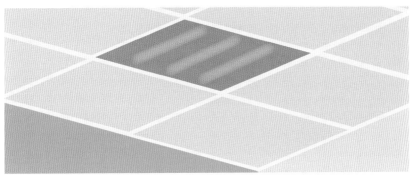

Fig 1.3 Luminaire installed in ceiling structure with a thermoplastic diffuser

The provisions regarding fire spread and internal linings do not include luminaires with diffusers that are attached to the soffit or suspended beneath a ceiling, as illustrated in Fig 1.4.

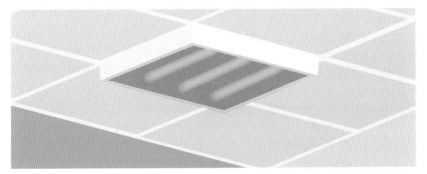

Fig 1.4 Surface mounted ceiling luminaire (non-structural)

It is important to check with the Local Authority Building Control to see what the required fire and acoustic performance is for the floor and ceiling and then to check with the manufacturer that the type of luminaire has adequate independent test and/or assessment evidence to support their claims. All luminaires must be fitted, taking account of the manufacturer's instructions as required by BS 7671 Regulation 510.3.

Requirements for Wales: Fire sprinkler systems
The Welsh Government amended Approved Document B volumes 1 and 2, with new Regulations and guidance that came into force on 1st January 2016.

The amendments to the documents are from the Domestic Fire Safety (Wales) Regulations, resulting in a new Section 7A 'Automatic Fire Suppression Systems' in the Building Regulations 2010 Statutory Instrument.

Section 7A introduces Regulations 37A and 37B, requiring all new 'domestic premises' to have a fire suppression system installed.

A fire suppression system is defined as an automatic system that controls and extinguishes fires without human intervention. Typically, these are sprinkler systems, although other types are available.

The requirements apply throughout Wales and apply to new build and change of use applications forming:

- New houses and flats
- Care homes
- Rooms for residential purposes (other than in a hotel, hospital, prison or short stay leisure hostel)
- Registered group homes and sheltered housing

The new Approved Documents note that the requirement to provide fire suppression is statutory. This means that sprinklers are mandatory, compensatory features cannot be added to the building to avoid their inclusion.

Requirement B3: Internal fire spread (structures)
States the following: The building shall be designed and constructed so that in the event of a fire, its stability will be maintained for a reasonable period.

Protection of openings and fire-stopping
Sections 7 and 8 of the Approved Document provides guidance on openings for pipes and fire-stopping.

In order to ensure fire-stopping elements of a building are effective. Every opening for services such as gas and water pipes and electricity cables to pass through should be adequately protected by sealing and fire-stopping so that the fire resistance is not impaired.

Therefore, any opening made for pipes, ducts, conduit, trunking, or cables should be:

- Kept as small as possible
- Fire-stopped

Fire-stopping

When a pipe or duct is fire-stopped, the materials used should allow for thermal movement. In order to prevent displacement, materials used for fire-stopping should be reinforced with, or supported by, materials of limited combustibility appropriate to the level of fire barrier required or in place.

Proprietary fire-stopping and sealing systems, which have been shown by test to maintain the fire resistance of a wall or other elements, are commercially available. Other materials which may be used are:

- Cement mortar
- Gypsum-based plaster
- Cement or gypsum-based vermiculite/perlite
- Glass fibre, crushed rock, blast furnace slag or ceramic-based products (with or without resin binders)
- Intumescent mastics

Any of these substances may be used if the situation is appropriate, but not all of them will be suitable for every situation.

Approved Document B does not state particular requirements for cables; however, the fire-stopping requirements should be applied for cables just the same as pipes. If an insulated and sheathed cable passes through a wall there is not necessarily a requirement to sleeve the cable with pipe, however, the hole size should be kept to a minimum, and any gaps around the cable should be suitably sealed.

BS 7671 Regulations 527.1.2 and 527.2.1, expressly requires that the fire stopping capability and rating of a structure or zone of a building, must not be impaired by the passage of cables or containment systems and should be coded accordingly on an EICR.

Installations involving trunking that pass through walls and floors need to be externally and internally sealed as in Fig 1.5.

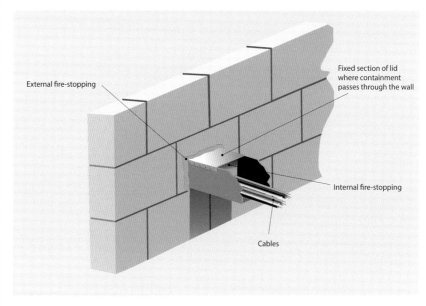

External fire-stopping

Fixed section of lid where containment passes through the wall

Internal fire-stopping

Cables

Fig 1.5 Trunking sealed internally and externally, to keep fire barrier integrity intact

1.7.5 Approved Document C – Site preparation and resistance to contaminants and moisture

The document is divided into two main requirements: C1 – Site preparation and resistance to contaminants C2 – Resistance to moisture

It is the requirement of C2, which may affect electrical installation work, and covers floors, walls, and the roof, as well as the people who use the building.

The structure shall adequately protect the building and people from harmful effects caused by:

- Ground moisture
- Precipitation and wind-driven spray
- Interstitial and surface condensation
- Spillage of water from or associated with sanitary fittings or fixed appliances

When installing wiring systems, care must be taken to ensure that any holes are sealed with a suitable sealing material to prevent penetration by rain or moisture.

Note

Where reference is made here to C1 and C2, this is directly made with reference to the sections of Approved Document C and is not a reference to a BS 7671 EICR Observation Code.

1.7.6 Approved Document E – Resistance to the passage of sound

The material used for sound absorption within a building usually has good thermal insulation properties. When installed within internal floors to resist the passage of sound, a number of risks are introduced for Electricians as follows:

- Creation of a fire risk when recessed lighting fittings are fitted in a ceiling which is covered by the material
- Sound may penetrate an internal floor of a building through a recessed light fitting
- The current-carrying capacity of circuit cables may be reduced considerably

1.7.7 Approved Document F – Ventilation

Ventilation systems for dwellings
Approved Document F provides guidance on four types of ventilation systems, as shown in Fig 1.6.

These are:

- System 1 – background ventilators and intermittent extract fans
- System 2 – passive stack ventilation
- System 3 – continuous mechanical extract
- System 4 – continuous mechanical supply and extract with heat recovery

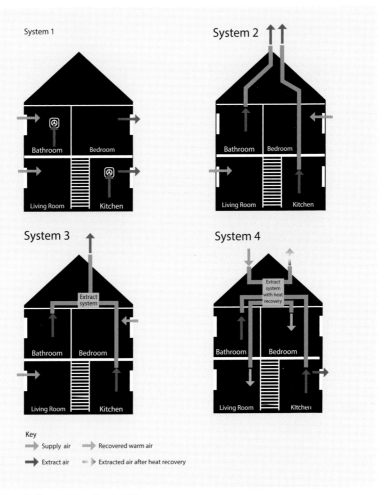

Fig 1.6 Ventilation systems for dwellings

For new buildings, extraction ventilation to the outside is required in each kitchen, utility room, bathroom and toilet. The extraction may operate intermittently or continuously. The minimum extraction airflow rates at the highest and lowest settings should not be less than those given in Table 1.4. Whole building ventilation rates are illustrated in Table 1.5.

Table 1.4 Building minimum extract rates

Extract ventilation rates	Intermittent extract	Continuous extract	
Room	Minimum extract rate (l/s)	Minimum high rate (l/s)	Minimum low rate (l/s)
Kitchen	30 adjacent to a hob; or 60 elsewhere	13	Total extract rate must be at least the whole dwelling ventilation rate in Table 1.5.
Utility room	30	8	
Bathroom	15	8	
Sanitary accommodation	6	6	

Table 1.5 Whole Dwelling ventilation rates

Whole dwelling ventilation rates (l/s)	Number of bedrooms
13	1
17	2
21	3
25	4
29	5

1.7.8 Approved Document L1A Conservation of fuel and power in new dwellings

Lighting installations covered by the Approved Document are fixed internal lighting and fixed external lighting.

Fixed internal lighting

For new dwellings, fairly complex calculations are made with regards to the conservation of energy, and the designer will consider the proportion of low-energy lamps installed in the fixed lighting locations when calculating the dwellings emission rate (DER). The minimum amount considered to be a reasonable provision is given in the Domestic Building Services Compliance Guide as summarised below:

- Three per four of all light fittings in main dwelling spaces (75%)
- Low energy light fittings having a luminous efficacy greater than 45 lumens per circuit-watt, and a total output greater than 400 lamp lumens

The term circuit-watt includes the power consumed in lighting circuits by lamps and associated control gear.

Lighting fittings installed in cupboards, wardrobes and storage areas can be ignored.

A way of achieving compliance would be to provide lighting fittings such as LED, fluorescent, and compact fluorescent lighting fittings. Fortunately, the performance of lighting has come on in leaps and bounds over the last few years with LED lamps making the biggest advances. These fittings are now widely used and available at affordable prices providing instant lighting capable of frequent switching. Standard tungsten lamps are being phased out and are fast becoming a thing of the past in most households.

LED lamps have an outstanding operational lifetime expectation of sometimes up to 100,000 hours, with an estimated energy efficiency of 80% – 90% when compared to traditional lighting and conventional light bulbs. They are Eco-Friendly compared to other lamps that contain toxic chemicals and materials, for example, mercury that is dangerous for the environment.

Fixed external lighting
Covers lighting fixed to the external surfaces of the dwelling, which are supplied from the dwelling's electrical system.

Effective control and/or the use of efficient lamps should be installed such that:

- Lamp capacity does not exceed 100 W per light fitting and has automatic presence and daylight detection
- Efficacy is equal to or greater than 45 lumens per circuit-watt, and has a manual switch and automatic daylight control

1.7.9 Approved Document L1B Conservation of fuel and power in existing dwellings

Fixed internal lighting

A reasonable provision should be made for occupiers of dwellings to obtain the benefits of efficient electric lighting when a dwelling is created from a change of use of a building, or an existing lighting system is being replaced as part of a rewire.

One way of achieving this compliance would be to adopt the guidance stated in Approved Document L1A, summarised in the previous section 1.7.8.

Fixed external lighting

The requirements for fixed external lighting are the same as stated in Approved Document L1A, see 1.7.8.

Mechanical cooling

The requirements are the same as stated in the Approved Document L1A, see 1.7.8.

Commissioning of heating and hot water systems

The requirements are also the same as stated in the Approved Document L1A, see 1.7.8.

1.7.10 Approved Document M – Access to and use of buildings

Part M of the Building Regulations 2015 Including 2016 Amendments introduces three categories of dwellings:

- Category 1: Visitable dwellings
- Category 2: Accessible and adaptable dwellings
- Category 3: Wheelchair user dwellings

Approved Document M requires reasonable provision to be made to enable people to gain access to and use a building and its facilities.

Services and controls

You should be aware that there are different requirements for the positioning of accessories, switches, and socket-outlets in each of the three categories of dwellings. These requirements set out the heights from the floor level for wall-mounted switches, socket-outlets, and any other equipment in habitable rooms, to enable persons with physical disabilities who have limited reach to be able to operate them.

Category 1 requires switches and socket-outlets, etc. to have their centre line 450-1200 mm above floor level, see Fig 1.7.

Category 2 has the same height requirement of 450-1200 mm; however, it also introduces the requirement of accessories being a minimum of 300 mm from an inside corner (measured horizontally), see Fig 1.8.

Category 3, to assist wheelchair users who have reduced reach. Switches and socket-outlets etc. should be located with their centre line 700-1000 mm above floor level and a minimum of 700 mm (measured horizontally) from an inside corner and should not be positioned behind appliances, see Fig 1.9.

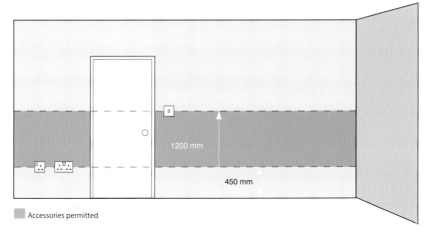

Accessories permitted

Fig 1.7 Category 1 accessory heights

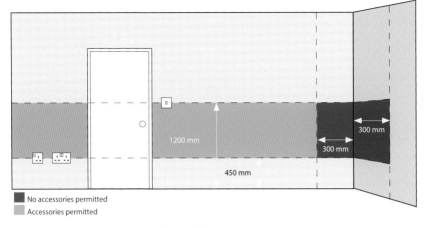

Fig 1.8 Category 2 accessory heights and distances

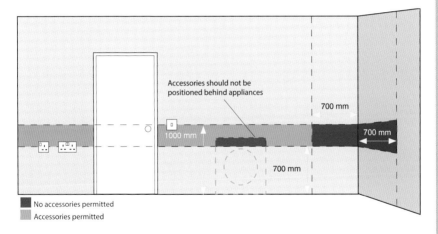

Fig 1.9 Category 3 accessory heights and distances

Consumer units

Consumer unit (CU) height requirements are the same for all three categories of dwellings. They should be mounted so that the switches are 1350-1450 mm above floor level.

Rewires, extensions, and alterations to existing installations

Part M does not apply to rewires, extensions, and alterations to existing electrical installations within a dwelling; however, on completion, it must be no worse with respect to Part M.

This allows Electricians to match existing heights and positions of accessories if desired by the Client. For example, if the existing accessories have been mounted at 300 mm, then the new accessories can be mounted at not less than 300 mm from floor level.

When carrying out an EICR, Inspectors must take this into account and remember the key elements of the EICR is to verify if an electrical installation is satisfactory for continued use, based upon historical use, current condition and the possibility that new requirements for safety may or may not positively affect the existing installation.

1.7.11 Approved Document P – Electrical safety

Approved Document P requires that reasonable provision shall be made in the design and installation of electrical installations in order to protect persons operating, maintaining or altering the installation from fire or injury.

There is a requirement that new installations and some additions and modifications to installations in dwellings in England and Wales be notified to the local building control. It should be noted that there is a slight difference between what is notifiable in England and Wales. This is due to Wales using the 2006 Approved Document and not adopting the updated 2013 version, see Figs 1.10 and 1.11. There is an exception in Wales for any building work carried out on 'excepted energy buildings', this must comply with Approved Document P 2013.

Fig 1.10 Wales Approved Document P 2006 edition amended to 2010

Fig 1.11 England Approved Document P 2013 edition

1.7.12 The Building (Scotland) Regulations 2004

The Building (Scotland) Regulations 2004 are made under the power of the Building (Scotland) Act 2003. They apply to the design, construction, or demolition of a building, the provision of services, fittings or equipment in or in connection with a building, and the conversion of a building.

Local authorities are appointed as verifiers of the building standard system under the Building (Scotland) Act 2003. The Building Standard department of the Local Authority carries out this role.

This page has been intentionally left blank

Section 2

BS 7671:2018+A1(2020) Requirements for
Electrical Installations

2.0 BS 7671:2018+A1(2020) Requirements for Electrical Installations

British Standard (BS) 7671:2018, also known as the IET Wiring Regulations, contains the requirements for electrical installations. The Regulations are non-statutory. However, they may be used in a court of law in evidence to claim compliance with the statutory requirements of the Electricity at Work Regulations.

Furthermore, Approved Document P of the Building Regulations states that electrical installation work to be designed and installed in accordance with BS 7671.

The Standard contains detailed technical information about the requirements for electrical installations and applies to installations up to 1000 V AC or 1500 V DC.

When a contract specifies that an installation is required to conform to BS 7671, the Standard becomes a legal requirement.

As the requirements of BS 7671 change, Electricians must keep themselves fully up to date with the latest amendments. For an Electrical Installation Inspector, it is extremely important to maintain an up to date knowledge of BS 7671, particularly Part 6, which specifically covers Inspection and Testing.

Part 6 of BS 7671 has two sections, Chapter 64 covering Initial Verification and Chapter 65 Periodic Inspection and Testing. They have very different requirements and the lead into each Chapter is worth understanding here before any work is started.

Chapter 64 Initial Verification

This Chapter requires that upon completion, and during installation and erection of the installation, inspection, and testing is carried out to verify the installation complies with BS 7671, as far as is reasonably practicable. Interestingly, this allows a practicability aspect to be used during erection and installation, as it may not always be practicable to test everything, until completion.

Chapter 65 Periodic Inspection and Testing

This Chapter advises that where necessary, the electrical inspection should be routinely inspected and tested to ensure it is in a satisfactory condition for continued use. Again, the reasonable practicability of this task is highlighted. Worth noting also is that Regulation 651.2 states that inspection shall be carried out, without dismantling of the installation, or with only partial dismantling, as is necessary; which means BS 7671 does not call for a complete strip-down of an installation in order to carry out an EICR, contrary to popular belief.

2.1 BS EN 61557 Electrical safety in low voltage distribution systems up to 1000 V AC. and 1500 V DC Equipment for testing, measuring or monitoring of protective measures

This suite of Standards prescribes the various attributes and tolerances that all electrical inspection test equipment must be designed and manufactured to. Although not technically within the scope of required knowledge for an Electrical Inspector, a working understanding of its basic principles is preferable.

When specifying, hiring or purchasing test equipment for a designated task or process, in accordance with BS 7671, the Inspector should confirm in all cases that the test equipment being used or proposed for use, fulfils the relevant parts of the BS EN 61557 series of Standards.

Not doing this could result in substandard test equipment being used or not adequately rated for the voltages that could be present, which in some cases could be fatal.

Where test equipment meets a different or similar standard to BS EN 61557, or where a manufacturer states conformity or compliance, that conformity should be requested and confirmed, before such equipment is used.

2.2 HSE Guidance Note: GS 38 Electrical test equipment for use on low voltage electrical systems

Possibly one of the most important pieces of guidance affecting Electrical Inspectors, HSE GS 38 gives requirements and advice on the selection and use of measuring equipment for circuits not exceeding 1000 V AC, specifically the component parts of that equipment, covering the following:

- Test probes
- Leads
- Clips/clamps
- Lamps
- Voltage detecting devices

There are very specific GS 38 requirements for these types of equipment, covering but not restricted to:

- Probe length
- Fusing of probes
- Maximum length of exposed metal parts of probes
- Lead insulation
- Lead flexibility
- Lead length
- Types of protective shroud
- Voltage indicating devices
- Socket and terminal testing equipment

Along with these requirements, GS 38 explains the need for safe systems of work, risk assessments prior to any testing, and the need to assess the correct level of PPE and that it is available.

Precautions to be taken during testing are also covered.

There is a popular misconception that GS 38 only covers the types of leads and probes that should be used with test equipment, whereas in reality, it is very much more than that, and its contents should be fully understood and adhered to by anyone involved in electrical installation inspection and testing.

This page has been intentionally left blank

Section 3

Identification of distribution equipment and installation components

3.0 Identification of Distribution equipment and installation components

Supplies of Electricity
During the inspection process, Inspectors will need to comment on the external condition of the installation intake equipment. Intake equipment is typically owned by three different bodies, which are:

- The distribution network operator (DNO),
- The electricity supplier (that's who the bill is paid to)
- The meter operator.

Inspectors often advise clients on their findings in this area and suggest appropriate actions that may be required. Having knowledge of the entire installation is vital to be able to give the correct advice regarding the next steps.

Distribution Network Operators (DNOs)
The electricity network service cable and cut-out are owned by the DNO, of which there are several. These are essentially the old regional electricity boards, and they report to:

- The Department for Business, Innovation, and Skills (formerly DTI)
- The Health and Safety Executive (HSE)
- OFGEM, which is the regulator of the gas and electricity industries in the UK.

The network operators are individually licensed by OFGEM. In its drive for increased efficiency, OFGEM has introduced competition to reduce costs to consumers. An example of this is that independent distribution network operators have been licensed by OFGEM. This means that more than one DNO could operate within a region. Network operators are responsible for work up to and including the main cut-out.

The network operators fund the Energy Network Association (ENA), which seeks to standardise practices amongst them. The ENA has no executive power and does not police the operators. The ENA website lists the operators and information concerning their policies: www.energynetworks.org

Electricity suppliers

Electricity suppliers sell electricity to the customer and are primarily responsible for customer contact. There are many licensed suppliers of electricity and gas in the UK.

Inspectors can find out who the electricity supplier is for the premises that they are working in by asking the Client/Duty holder who the bill is paid to. Electricity suppliers are not responsible for work on the consumer's side of the cut-out, although they are authorised to withdraw and replace the main fuse.

The electricity suppliers generally contract out specific metering tasks, to meter operator companies. These services can include withdrawal and replacement of the main fuse and fitting of double-pole isolators see Fig 3.1. Details of the Electricity Suppliers can be found at https://www.energy-uk.org.uk/

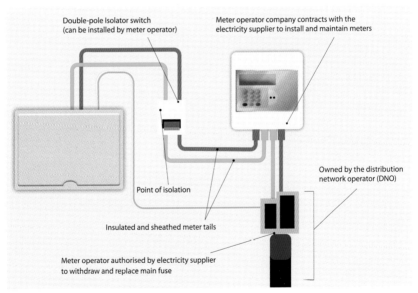

Fig 3.1 Double-pole isolator between cut-out and CU

Meter operators

Meter operators are agents of the electricity suppliers. A contract exists between the suppliers and their meter operators, which allows suitably trained meter operators to withdraw the main fuse for temporary disconnection and then replace it after any work has been completed.

This may require a second visit, where the disconnection work is to allow a contractor to fit or modify the consumers' installation, which is usually the Distribution equipment/Consumer Unit (CU).

Most meter operators who visit premises to withdraw the main fuse, as an alternative, can install a double-pole isolator between the meter and the consumer unit if requested to do so on the same visit. This allows the consumer's installation to be isolated by the consumer's contractor to carry out any modifications, without needing a Meter Operators employee to be present.

Supply Earthing systems
The three most common types of supply systems found in UK properties are:

- TN-S
- TN-C-S
- TT

TN-S system
Typical maximum supply characteristics quoted by DNO:

- Z_e 0.8 Ω
- I_{pf} 16 kA

TN-S systems have separate neutral and protective conductors for the supply, with the centre point of the transformer directly earthed. The earth connection is via the cable sheath, as illustrated in Fig 3.2.

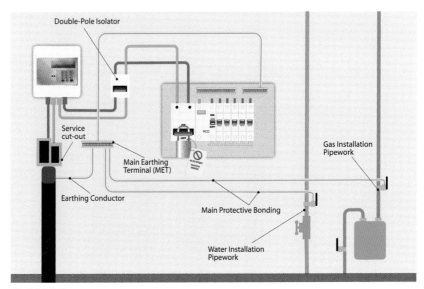

Fig 3.2 TN-S system

TN-C-S system

Typical maximum supply characteristics quoted by DNO:

- Z_e 0.35 Ω
- I_{pf} 16 kA

TN-C-S systems have the neutral and protective functions combined in a single conductor known as the Protective Earth Neutral conductor (PEN). This arrangement is on the supply system only and then is separated at the service head, as illustrated in Fig 3.3.

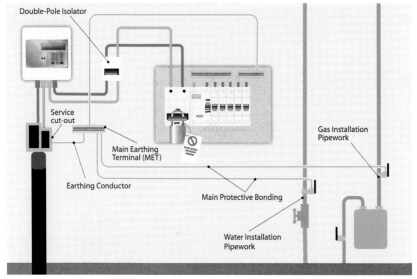

Fig 3.3 TN-C-S system

TT systems

TT systems have one point of the source of energy, typically the transformer in the sub-station, directly earthed (21 Ω is usually quoted as the maximum for this position). With exposed-conductive-parts of the installation connected to the consumer earth electrode(s), which needs to have an electrode resistance as low as possible. BS 7671 suggests that Earth electrode resistances may be unsuitable above 200 Ω. Remember that electrode resistance will be affected by changes in the environment. See Fig 3.4.

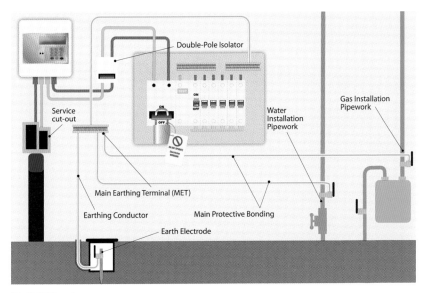

Fig 3.4 TT system

3.1 Consumer unit designs

Consumer units are available for purchase in various configurations to suit different installations and budgets. They have also evolved through the years, and it is important for inspectors to be familiar with the various configurations that they will come across during inspections.

A consumer unit, is a specific type of distribution board intended to be operated by ordinary persons conforming to BS EN 61439-3 and having a rated conditional short-circuit current of 16 kA under specific installation arrangements. For further guidance on consumer unit and distribution board application, please see BEAMA Technical Bulletin - Consumer Unit 16 kA Conditional Rating Application.

Understanding the history of these changes will indicate which Edition of BS 7671 the installation was designed to. The common types are listed as follows:

Flexible split load consumer units
These first became popular in BS 7671:2001, consisting of a 100 A main switch providing a number of ways that were non-RCD protected and a selection of ways that were RCD protected. The split was adjustable. See Fig 3.5.

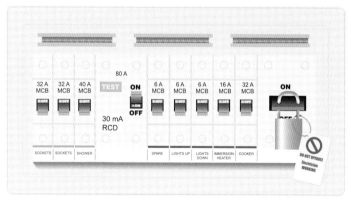

Fig 3.5 Split load consumer unit, typical 16th Edition configuration

In the BS 7671:2001, lighting circuits typically would not require 30 mA RCDs for additional protection. This was due to the possibility of unwanted tripping, leading to the scenario of people being left in the dark, which could be dangerous.

In BS 7671:2008, more requirements for using 30 mA RCD protection were introduced, meaning that additional RCD protection now applied to lighting circuits where any cables (including switch drops) were at a depth of less than 50 mm from the surface in the wall. This would see the birth of the dual RCD unit.

Dual RCD consumer units

These are readily available, affordable and have been generally accepted in the industry as meeting the 'division of installation requirements' of Regulation 314.1. The unit comes with a 100 A main switch that feeds two 30 mA RCDs, allowing circuits to be split over both RCDs. See Fig 3.6.

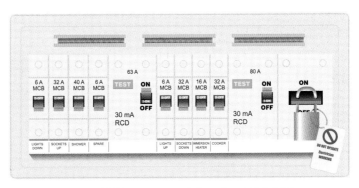

Fig 3.6 Dual RCD consumer unit introduced 17th Edition

High integrity dual RCD consumer units

These are more flexible than the dual RCD type. The unit also comes with a main switch that feeds two 30 mA RCDs however there is an additional advantage of having a number of circuits fed directly from the main switch. Therefore, giving options to further sub-divide the installation. For these unprotected ways, Electricians may choose to either use circuit-breakers or RCBOs depending on the application. See Fig 3.7.

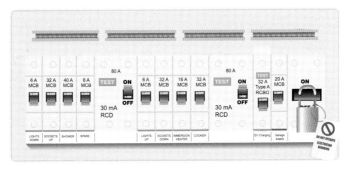

Fig 3.7 High integrity consumer unit, providing design flexibility

RCBO consumer unit

This type of consumer unit configuration is considered to be the best, after BS 7671:2018 introduced requirements for the design of installations to avoid unwanted tripping of RCDs. Regulation 531.3.2 states that residual current protective devices shall be selected and erected such as to limit the risk of unwanted tripping.

A number of considerations are given, with the first two summarised below:

1. Subdivision of circuits with individual associated RCDs (the RCBO CU meets this)

2. To avoid unwanted tripping the accumulation of protective conductor currents and/or earth leakage currents downstream of the RCD shall be not more than 30% of the rated residual operating current

Using 30% of a 30 mA RCD gives a maximum allowable amount of 9 mA leakage for normal operation. Although this requirement may be hard to meet if you have several circuits protected by one RCD and you don't know what equipment will be used in the installation. See Fig 3.8 RCBO consumer unit, considered to be the best approach.

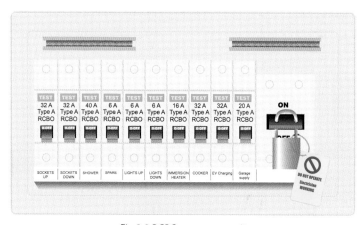

Fig 3.8 RCBO consumer unit

The 18th Edition Consumer Unit

Requirements introduced with BS 7671:2018 have meant that further consideration is needed for the correct selection of consumers units.

Historically devices such as RCCBs and Main Switches have relied on diversity with regards to their current rating; however, no consideration was given to their protection against overload.

In commercial and industrial applications, switchgear is usually backed up by another device providing overload protection. As can be seen in the example distribution block diagram in Fig 3.9.

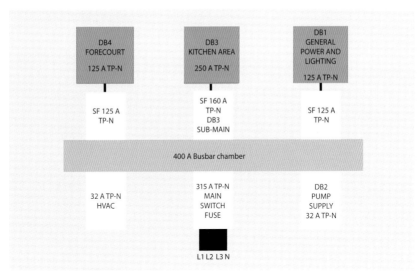

Fig 3.9 Example distribution block diagram

Residential distribution is different, usually, the consumer unit is connected directly to the meter tails with no additional OCPD fitted, but not always, as in the case of flats fed by a switch fuse.

Unless the upstream protection is known to be 60/63 A (fuse or CB), traditional consumer units with 63/80 A RCCBs won't fully meet the requirements of BS 7671:2018. This is because Regulation 536.4.3.2 states that RCCBs and Main Switches do not provide protection against overload, and therefore, they shall be protected by an OCPD.

Furthermore, Regulation 536.4.202 states that overload protection shall not solely be based on the use of diversity factors of the downstream circuits, and the rating of the overcurrent protective device shall be selected according to the manufacturer's instructions.

Inspectors will need to be aware of the different installation approaches that achieve compliance with Regulation 536.4.202; the following options are appropriate:

1. Specify a consumer unit with 100 A rated main switch and RCCBs. This will allow the unit to be fitted without any further considerations regarding overload protection

2. Use an RCBO consumer unit (consideration is still needed regarding the rating of the main switch)

3. Guarantee that the total sum of the rated current of downstream CBs does not exceed the rating of the main switch or RCCB. It is important to note that any spare ways could compromise relying on this method; if additional loads were to be added, see Fig 3.10 for clarity

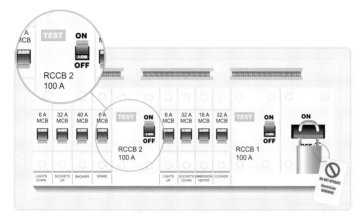

Fig 3.10 18th Edition consumer unit, showing rating of devices for incoming supply

Consumer units/distribution boards and components

Inspectors will need to be able to identify various components and understand their operating characteristics as part of the inspection process. This section lists the main components of distribution boards and consumer units and provides commentary on BS 7671.

Switch disconnector (main switch)

Regulation 132.15.201 requires that an effective means, suitably placed for ready operation, shall be provided so that all voltage may be cut off from every installation, from every circuit, and from all equipment, to prevent or remove danger.

For consumer units, this is usually the switch on the far side of the consumer unit (often with a red toggle), which isolates both the incoming line and neutral conductors as required by Regulation 462.1.201. The current rating of these switch disconnectors is usually 100 A but must be confirmed to be so.

Three-phase distribution boards generally have 3-pole switch disconnectors that isolate all line conductors but not the neutral. This is fine for TN-C-S and TN-S systems providing protective bonding is installed, and the neutral conductor is reliably connected to Earth by a low resistance see Regulation 461.2.

For installations forming part of a TT or IT system, isolation is required for all live conductors, and therefore the neutral will have to be disconnected requiring a 4-pole switch. Current ratings start at 100 A. Different types of standard isolators can be seen in Fig 3.11.

Fig 3.11 Types of 2-pole, 3-pole and 4-pole isolators

Circuit-breakers (BS EN 60898)

Circuit-breakers (CBs) are responsible for protecting individual circuits against electrical faults and overcurrent.

The consumer unit should be clearly labelled to indicate which CB protects each circuit of the electrical installation, either by writing in the space provided or by using sticky labels, which is a requirement of BS 7671 Regulation 514.9.1.

A simple chart based on the test schedule may be used to satisfy these requirements, and this should be provided on or adjacent to the consumer unit.

As part of the inspection process, it will need to be verified that the correct type and rating of CBs are installed. The minimum checks required are:

- Correctly sized conductors for the installed conditions (in relation to CB current rating)
- CB able to provide fault protection
- Correct Type of CB (suitable for the nature of the load)
- Adequate short-circuit capacity rating

Duty rating of circuit-breakers to BS EN 60898 and RCBOs to BS EN 61009

Two rated short-circuit capacities may be quoted I_{cn} or I_{cs}

- I_{cn} The rated ultimate short-circuit capacity is the maximum fault current the circuit-breaker can safety interrupt, although the device may be damaged and no longer useable.

- I_{cs} The rated service short-circuit breaking capacity is the maximum level of fault current the circuit-breaker can interrupt without loss of performance of the circuit-breaker.

Duty Ratings of BS 3871, BS EN 60898 and BS EN 61009 devices are given in Table 3.1, and common application of BS 3871 and BS EN 60898 devices are given in Table 3.2.

The circuit-breaker will be marked with the I_{cn} value (rated service short-circuit capacity). The value will appear inside a rectangle without a unit symbol, e.g.

Table 3.1 Duty rating capacities of circuit-breakers – BS 3871, BS EN 60898 and RCBOs to BS EN 61009

Miniature circuit-breakers (BS 3871 – part 1)		CBs to BS EN 60898 and RCBOs to BS EN 61009	
Category of duty	Rated capacity (kA)	I_{cn}	I_{cs}
		Marked on device	Rated capacity (kA)
M 1	1	1.5	1.5
M 1.5	1.5	3	3
M 3	3	6	6
M 4.5	4.5	10	7.5
M 6	6	15	7.5
M 9	9	20	10
		25	12.5

Typical applications and ratings for circuit-breakers to BS 3871 and BS EN 60898

Table 3.2 Circuit-breaker applications – BS 3871 and BS EN 60898	
Type	Application
1 B	General domestic and commercial installations with little or no switching surges
2 3 C	General commercial and industrial installations where fluorescent lighting and small motors produce switching surges
4 D	For use where high inrush currents could happen e.g. transformers, industrial welding equipment, x-ray machines, etc.

Fuses

In many older installations, you find these more often, you will find fuses instead of circuit-breakers providing fault protection for circuits. There are two types of fuses commonly found:

Cartridge fuse to BS 1361

BS 1361 Type II fuses are commonly found in the distributors' cut-out; however, it will be fuses to BS 1361 Type I that are encountered in fuse boxes. Maximum earth fault loop impedance values are not given in BS 7671 since such devices were replaced by BS 88 fuses (see below). For inspectors requiring Max Z_s values for this device, refer to Table 3.3 (NAPIT's maximum measured earth fault loop impedance chart), this is also reproduced in Appendix 2 of this guide for ease of use.

Table 3.3 80% device Z$_s$ values

Overcurrent protective device (OCPD) Rating AMPS	PROTECTIVE DEVICE TYPE & BS EN NUMBER													
	BS 88-2		BS 88-3		BS 3036		BS 1361/2		BS 3871 TYPE			BS EN 60898 BS EN 61009-1		
	E bolt & G clip		Fuse Sys. C		Fuse		Fuse		1	2	3	B	C*	D*
							BS 1362 (Plug Top)							
	0.4 s	5 s	0.4 s	5 s	0.4 s	5 s	0.4 s	5 s	0.4/5 s	0.4/5 s	0.4/5 s	0.4/5 s	0.4/5 s	0.4 s
2	26.5	35.2	N/A	N/A	N/A	N/A	N/A	N/A	N/A	N/A	N/A	N/A	N/A	N/A
3	N/A	N/A	N/A	N/A	N/A	N/A	12.48	17.60	N/A	N/A	N/A	11.66	N/A	N/A
4	12.5	16.8	N/A	N/A	N/A	N/A	N/A	N/A	N/A	N/A	N/A	N/A	N/A	N/A
5	N/A	N/A	7.94	11.68	7.28	13.44	7.94	12.44	8.74	4.99	3.50	N/A	N/A	N/A
6	6.24	9.60	N/A	N/A	N/A	N/A	N/A	N/A	7.22	4.08	2.91	5.82	2.91	1.45
10	3.72	5.44	N/A	N/A	N/A	N/A	N/A	N/A	4.37	2.50	1.75	3.49	1.75	0.87
13	N/A	N/A	N/A	N/A	N/A	N/A	1.83	2.90	N/A	N/A	N/A	N/A	N/A	N/A
15	N/A	N/A	N/A	N/A	1.94	4.06	2.48	3.8	2.85	1.66	1.16	N/A	N/A	N/A
16	1.94	3.20	1.84	3.12	N/A	N/A	N/A	N/A	2.66	1.56	1.09	2.18	1.09	0.54
20	1.34	2.24	1.54	2.56	1.34	2.91	1.29	2.13	2.18	1.25	0.87	1.75	0.87	0.44
25	1.03	1.76	N/A	N/A	N/A	N/A	N/A	N/A	1.75	1.00	0.70	1.39	0.69	0.35
30	N/A	N/A	N/A	N/A	0.83	2.00	0.87	1.39	1.46	0.83	0.58	N/A	N/A	N/A
32	0.79	1.36	0.73	1.28	N/A	N/A	N/A	N/A	1.37	0.78	0.55	1.10	0.55	0.27
40	0.60	1.04	N/A	N/A	N/A	N/A	N/A	N/A	1.09	0.62	0.44	0.87	0.44	0.22
45	N/A	N/A	0.46	0.80	0.45	1.20	N/A	0.72	0.97	0.55	0.39	0.77	0.38	0.19
50	0.46	0.79	N/A	N/A	N/A	N/A	N/A	N/A	0.87	0.50	0.35	0.69	0.35	0.17
60	N/A	N/A	N/A	N/A	0.32	0.86	N/A	0.53	N/A	N/A	N/A	N/A	N/A	N/A
63	0.35	0.62	0.29	0.54	N/A	N/A	N/A	N/A	0.69	0.40	0.28	0.55	0.28	0.13
80	N/A	0.44	N/A	0.41	N/A	N/A	N/A	0.38	0.55	0.31	0.22	0.43	0.22	0.10
100	N/A	0.34	N/A	0.30	N/A	0.40	N/A	0.26	0.44	0.25	0.17	0.34	0.17	0.07
125	N/A	0.26	N/A	N/A	N/A	N/A	N/A	N/A	N/A	N/A	N/A	0.27	0.13	0.06
160	N/A	0.21	N/A	N/A	N/A	N/A	N/A	N/A	N/A	N/A	N/A	N/A	N/A	N/A
200	N/A	0.14	N/A	N/A	N/A	N/A	N/A	N/A	N/A	N/A	N/A	N/A	N/A	N/A
250	N/A	N/A	N/A	N/A	N/A	N/A	N/A	N/A	N/A	N/A	N/A	N/A	N/A	N/A

*For BS EN 60898 / 61009 Type 'D' 5 Sec. Please use Type 'C' Column.

Cartridge fuse to BS 88

Fuse boxes containing fuses to BS 88-3 fuse system C are found in dwellings. These are the cylindrical type of fuse and not the bolted or clip-in type of fuse that is used in many commercial and industrial applications. BS 7671 still recognises this series of fuse, and maximum earth fault loop impedance values are given in BS 7671:2018 Tables 41.2 and 41.4, for 0.4 s and 5 s disconnection time respectively.

The body of the fuse is ceramic with metal end caps to which the fuse element is connected as illustrated in Fig 3.12.

Fig 3.12 BS 88-3 C Fuse and carrier

Fuse systems BS 88-2 G (clip in) and E (bolt in) are illustrated in Fig 3.13.

Fuse system G   Fuse system E

Fig 3.13 BS 88-2 G (clip in) and E (bolt in)

Semi-enclosed rewireable fuse to BS 3036

The body of the fuse is manufactured from ceramic or plastic material to which two brass contacts are attached and a tinned copper fuse wire is connected as illustrated in Fig 3.14.

The diameter of the fuse wires to be used as a fuse element is given in Table 533.1 of BS 7671 for different fuse ratings, for inspectors verifying correct sizes on-site, see Table 3.4.

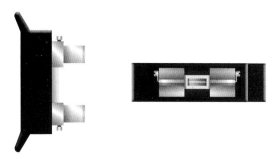

Fig 3.14 BS 3036 semi-enclosed rewireable fuse

Table 3.4 Fuse wire sizes vs rating	
Rated current of fused elements (A)	**Nominal diameter of wire (mm)**
3	0.15
5	0.2
10	0.35
15	0.5
20	0.6
25	0.75
30	0.85
45	1.25
60	1.53
80	1.8
100	2.0

Residual Current Devices

Residual Current Device (RCD) is the generic term for many devices capable of operation when subjected to a predetermined value.

Inspectors will need to identify what purpose the RCD fulfils to be able to verify if the correct type and rating has been installed.

RCD requirements

BS 7671 specifies RCDs for three reasons:

- Fault protection
- Additional protection
- Fire protection

Fault protection

RCDs are used where the earth fault loop impedance is too high for the overcurrent protective device to meet the required disconnection time. For example, in a TT system where the earth electrode impedance will be greater than the maximum Z_s of the protective device.

Table 41.5 of BS 7671 gives the maximum earth fault loop impedance for non-delayed and time-delayed S Type RCDs, this is summarised in Table 3.5.

Table 3.5 Maximum Earth fault loop impedance values for RCDs	
Rated residual operating current (mA)	Maximum earth fault loop impedance Z_s (ohms)
30	1667
100	500
300	167
500	100

Additional protection

RCDs rated at 30 mA, or less are used in more onerous situations, primarily to protect life. Regulation 643.8 contains a Note, requiring that RCDs meeting the requirements of 415.1.1, disconnect within 40 ms when subjected to a test current of at least 5 $I_{\Delta n}$.

The following requirements are the reason why most circuits within dwellings require additional protection by use of a 30 mA RCD:

- Cables installed at a depth of less than 50 mm from the surface without additional requirements being met (Regulation 522.6.202)
- Cables installed at any depth in a wall or partition with metallic parts without additional requirements being met (Regulation 522.6.203)
- Socket-outlets with a rated current not exceeding 32 A (Regulation 411.3.3)
- Mobile equipment used outdoors with a rated current not exceeding 32 A (Regulation 411.3.3)

- Circuits serving locations containing a bath or shower or circuits passing through Zones 1 and/or 2 not serving the location (Regulation 701.411.3.3)
- All AC final circuits supplying luminaires (Regulation 411.3.4)
- Swimming pools and other basins Zones 0, 1 and 2 (Section 702)
- Rooms and cabins containing sauna heaters (Section 703)

Fire protection

RCDs rated at 300 mA, or less are used as a measure for protection against fire. This requirement is not just restricted to commercial and industrial installations; it is likely to be applicable to any dwellings with outbuildings used for agricultural or horticultural purposes, see Regulation 705.422.7.

BS 7671 Section 532 Devices for protection against the risk of fire, provides further requirements.

The RCD test button

As the operation of the RCD relies on a mechanical system, regular testing is required. To this end, RCDs have a test button incorporated to facilitate this. This is one of the functional tests to be carried out during the inspection process, as well as checking that a label is fixed in a prominent position at, or near, each RCD in the installation to show that the installation, or part of it, is protected by a residual current device, and it must be tested six-monthly by pressing the button marked 'T' or 'Test.'

Residual current circuit-breaker with overcurrent protection (RCBOs)

RCBOs combine the same overcurrent functions of a CB with the earth fault functions of an RCD all in one compact, single-unit device. A range of sensitivity and current ratings are available.

Like RCDs, it is recommended that RCBOs are tested on a regular basis by pressing the test button. When the test button is pressed, the device should trip and go into the off position. RCBOs also fulfil the function of a switch-disconnector for isolating the conductor of the line out-going circuit.

Types of RCD

Consumer units and distribution boards are commonly supplied with Type AC RCDs (unless another type is specified). Type AC RCDs are general-purpose RCDs that are not suited to all loads. Type AC RCDs are affected by normally occurring stray DC currents, produced by certain types of equipment. When stray DC currents are present, an AC type RCD will not register residual current flowing in the cpc. Stray DC current effectively masks the alternating residual current the AC device is looking for, and it will not operate.

Regulation 531.3.3 gives requirements for RCD selection and states that different types of RCD exist, depending on their behaviour in the presence of DC components and frequencies. The appropriate RCD shall be selected.

Industry guidance for testing RCDs has always been to ensure that equipment is not connected to them and that the RCD is effectively alone in its circuit. This protocol is no longer strictly accurate, and other factors now need to be taken into account.

There are significantly different types of RCDs now available, and they are designed for differing equipment types. It is vital that as an Inspector, you know what their differences are and how they should be used. Table 3.6 lays out the different RCD types and examples of equipment types that they are designed to operate with.

Table 3.6 Types of RCD and their operating restrictions and marking symbols

RCD	Symbol	Examples of type of equipment / load
Type AC		Resistive, Capacitive, Inductive loads generally without any electronic components, typically: • Immersion heater • Oven/Hob with resistive heating elements • Electric shower • Tungsten & halogen lighting
Type A		Single-phase with electronic components, typically: • Single-phase invertors • Class I IT and Multimedia equipment • Power supplies for Class II equipment • Appliances such as a washing machine that is not frequency controlled e.g. DC or universal motor • Lighting controls such as a dimmer switch and home and building electronic systems LED drivers • Induction hobs • Electric Vehicle charging where any smooth DC fault current is less than 6 mA • Electric vehicle charging in conjunction with RDC-DD **Type A is also suitable for Type AC applications.**
Type F		Frequency controlled equipment / appliances, typically: • Some washing machines, dishwashers and driers e.g. containing synchronous motors* • Some air conditioning controllers using variable frequency speed drives • Electric vehicle charging in conjunction with RDC-DD **Type F is also suitable for Type AC and Type A applications.**
Type B		Three-phase electronic equipment typically: • Inverters for speed control • UPS • Electric Vehicle charging where any smooth DC fault current is greater than 6 mA • Photovoltaic Power Electronic Converter Systems (PECS) typically: • Industrial machines • Cranes **Type B is also suitable for Type AC, Type A and Type F applications.**

* Manufacturer's instructions should be taken into account.

Power electronic converter PEC
Device or part thereof for the purpose of electronic power conversion, including signalling, measurement, control circuitries and other parts, if essential for the power conversion function

Power electronic converter system PECS
One or more power electronic converters intended to work together with other equipment
For PECS, if a Type B RCD is required, the product will be marked with the symbol ⚠.

The instructions shall include a caution notice highlighting that where an RCD is used for protection against electrical shock, only an RCD of Type B is allowed on the supply side of this product.

71

RCD selectivity

Selectivity is the ability of a protective device to operate in preference to another protective device in series. Inspectors will need to understand the requirements of Regulation 536.4.1.4 regarding selectivity between RCDs.

In the case of residual currents, where selectivity is required between RCDs the:

- The upstream RCD should be suitably time delayed, and
- The ratio of upstream to downstream residual current rating should be at least 3:1

Installing RCDs with different trigger ratings and or time-delayed devices is not a new concept. However, the major change within the 18th Edition of BS 7671 is the requirement to select the appropriate Type of RCD, dependent on the expected load. Correct coordination of Types of RCD is essential when in series also. In the absence of specific information from the device manufacturer, Fig 3.15 provides guidance on the selection of RCDs in series.

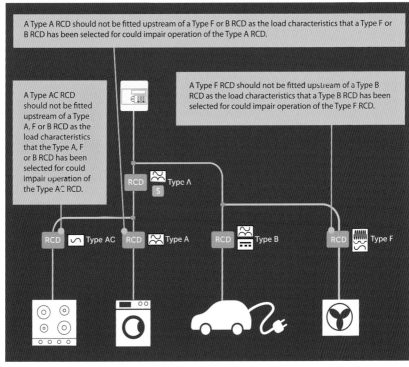

Fig 3.15 Selectivity of RCDs

Arc fault detection devices (AFDD)

Regulation 421.1.7 recommends the installation of arc fault detection devices (AFDDs) to mitigate the risk of fire in AC final circuits of a fixed installation due to the effects of arc fault currents. AFDDs can be installed in consumer units and distribution boards to protect final circuits; however, overcurrent protection and, if required, RCD's will still be needed.

Electrical fires can be caused by a number of issues requiring protection from more than one device:

- Short-circuits and overloads: Protection provided by CBs & Fuses
- Earth leakage currents: Protection by RCDs, RCBOs, etc
- Overvoltage: Protection by SPDs
- Dangerous electric arcs: Protection by AFDDs

It is a requirement that where AFDDs are fitted, they are fitted at the origin of the circuit they are protecting. As these devices start to appear on the market, inspectors will need to understand how they work and what their limitations are.

Appropriate ways to minimise the occurrence of arc faults must still be applied, such as:

- Correct cable installation in prescribed zones
- Correct cable radius on bends
- Correct terminal tightness
- Suitable intervals of periodic inspection (EICR)
- Regular inspection of appliances and flexible leads, etc. used in the installation

Surge protection devices (SPD)

As SPDs find their way into installations more frequently, we need to be aware of the very different ways they can be installed and the different types that are available. Not all SPDs are the same. Some devices are specifically designed for use in TT installations and must be fitted in the correct part of that installation, with regards to any RCDs, that are installed.

The changes included in BS 7671:2018 have included many changes to the way we choose and install different SPDs, which needs to be looked at carefully when we are carrying out EICRs.

Identification of Distribution equipment and installation components

A simple visual sighting of an SPD to confirm compliance, generally won't provide the information we need. We need to confirm that the SPD is:

- The correct type for the earthing system
- Installed in the correct position, respective to RCDs and the Main Earth Terminal (MET)
- Currently capable of operating, and its condition indicator is telling us this.

SPD Overcurrent protection

Attention is drawn to the OCPD in the surge circuit, known as the SPDA or surge protection device assembly.

Regulation 534.4.5.1 requires that SPD installations shall be protected against overcurrent with respect to short-circuit currents, and that the OCPD shall be the highest permissible rating to ensure a high surge current capability for the complete assembly.

This protection may be internal and/or external to the SPD according to the manufacturer's instructions. It is important to select OCPDs in accordance with the manufacturer's instructions to ensure compatibility.

Conductor and connection requirements

To achieve maximum performance of the device it is essential that all connections are kept as short and straight as possible, and any unnecessary cable loops shall be avoided.

The minimum conductor sizes (copper or equivalent conductor) needed for connection between SPD and MET are:

- 6 mm^2 for Type 2 SPDs, and
- 16 mm^2 for Type 1 SPDs

The total length of conductors between connection points of the SPD assembly should not exceed 0.5 m (preferably) and, in no case, exceed 1.0 m. If 0.5 m is exceeded, an SPD with lower voltage protection level U_p may be needed.

Where the MET is more than the required distance away for effective overvoltage control and reduced voltage protection levels (U_p), Inspectors need to understand that it is acceptable to use an intermediate earthing terminal to decrease the lead length of SPD supply conductors. The DB earth bar or an earth stud on the chassis or backplate are examples of an intermediate earth terminal, where the other attached cpcs will enable current division and reduce effects downstream.

A list of inspections required for SPDs is given in Table 3.7

Table 3.7 Surge Protection Device Inspection Check Routine	
Check No	Check to be carried out
1	Installed with PE cable not less than: 6 mm² for type 2 16 mm² for type 1 *Cable sized in accordance with Regulation 543.4.10 as a minimum*
2	Cables should preferably not exceed 0.5 m and in no case, exceed 1.0 m in length. See BS 7671 Regulation 534.4.8
3	Where cables are exceeding the requirements in 2 above, that the provision of an intermediate earth terminal (when appropriate) or additional SPDs have been installed closer to the equipment to be protected. See BS 7671 figure 534.9. Care should be taken here as the method in figure 534.9 is low current use only, generally 100 A or less, as determined by the terminals current rating. Under the product standard BS EN 61643, the label of the SPD shall have some specific information see BS 7671 Figure 5.6.1
4	Status indication window to be checked, if defective or indicates that the SPD is no longer operational (usually by a red label or tell-tale) the SPD may need to be to be replaced (depending on the requirements of the client and the use of the installation). Some SPDs have LED illuminated indication, in power down testing the LED is off, so true status cannot be determined until power is restored.
5	Fuse size for SPD circuit is shown, check that lower rated fuses are not fitted as this would degrade SPD performance. Check the fuse/OCPD is intact/operational and that, in line with BS 7671 Regulation 534.4.4.7, the whole SPD assembly (SPDA) is rated not less than the prospective short-circuit current at the location. (recommend replacement based on Client requirements).
6	Check that any isolator in surge circuit is closed.

Table 3.7 Surge Protection Device Inspection Check Routine (cont).

7	SPD is labelled with an indicated T1 or T2 or T3 in a square denoting its type (see Fig 3.16). T1 at the origin/origins of metallic services if the structure has a fitted lightning protection system. T2 at origin/origins where LPS is not fitted and further locations where cables cross internal zonal interfaces. T3 for locations closer to the end user equipment and not greater than 10 m from the end user equipment.
8	Check that the kA value (I_{nspd}) of the SPD is in accordance with: 1. BS 7671 Regulation 534.4.4.4.1 for type 2 SPD at 5 kA per pole in CT1 connection methods. 2. BS 7671 Regulation 534.4.4.4.2 for type 1 SPDs with a value of 12.5 kA (I_{imp}) per pole in CT1 connection methods. Reference to both Regulations for the CT2 values in TT supplies.

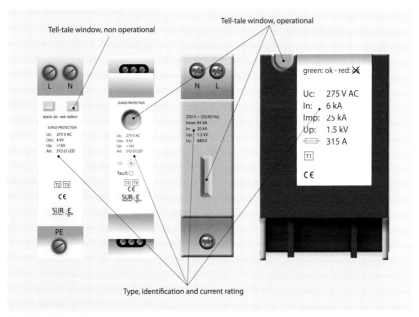

Fig 3.16 SPD markings

Protective Earthing and Bonding

Bonding is not the same as earthing. Although green and yellow conductors are used in earthing and bonding, they are different.

3.2 Protective Earthing

One of the methods used to provide fault protection against electric shock in the event of insulation failure is to provide protective earthing. Earthing of a point or points in an installation, or in equipment for purposes of safety, can be achieved using a combination of an earthing conductor and circuit protective conductors to connect exposed-conductive-parts to Earth using a main earthing terminal (MET). These conductors and conductive-parts are defined as:

Circuit protective conductor (cpc)
A protective conductor connecting exposed-conductive-parts of equipment to the main earthing terminal.

Earth
The conductive mass of the Earth, whose electrical potential at any point is conventionally taken at zero.

Earthing
A connection of exposed-conductive-parts of an installation to the main earthing terminal of that installation.

Earth electrode
A conductive part, which may be embedded in the soil or in a specific conductive medium; for example, concrete, in electrical contact with Earth.

Earthing conductor
A protective conductor connecting the main earthing terminal of an installation to an earth electrode or other means of earthing.

Exposed-conductive-parts
The conductive part of equipment which can be touched, and which is not normally live, but which can become live under fault conditions.

Main earthing terminal (MET)
The terminal or bar provided for the connection of protective conductors, including protective bonding conductors, and conductors for functional earthing, if any, to the means of earthing. In larger installations, these may be referred to as 'Earth Marshalling Bars', where numerous connections may be required.

Protective Bonding

When installing electrical installations in buildings with extraneous-conductive-parts such as metalwork of other services (e.g., gas, water, oil, heating, air conditioning pipework and ducting, etc.) it is necessary to ensure that all this metalwork is maintained at substantially the same potential. To this end, protective bonding needs to be carried out using protective equipotential bonding conductors. These conductors and conductive-parts are defined as:

Equipotential bonding

Electrical connection maintaining various exposed-conductive-parts and extraneous-conductive-parts at substantially the same potential.

Extraneous-conductive-parts

A conductive part liable to introduce a potential, generally Earth potential, and not forming part of the electrical installation.

Protective conductor (PE)

A conductor used for some measure of protection against electrical shock and intended for connecting together any of the following parts:

- Earth electrode(s)
- The earthed point of the source or an artificial neutral
- The main earthing terminal
- Exposed-conductive-parts
- Extraneous-conductive-parts

Protective bonding conductor

A protective conductor providing equipotential bonding.

For examples of protective earthing and equipotential bonding see Fig 3.17.

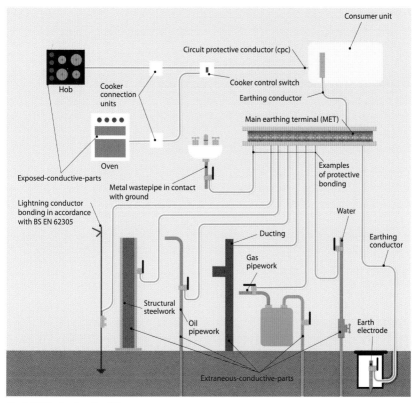

Fig 3.17 Protective Earthing system

Regulation 411.3.1.2 States that metallic pipes entering the building having an insulating section at their point of entry need not be connected to the protective equipotential bonding. There is also no requirement to bond plastic pipes entering the building, such as blue water service pipes.

However, if the pipework in the building is metallic and re-enters the ground (e.g., heating pipes in screed concrete, etc.), then they would require bonding at the position they reappear out of the ground. Alternatively, they would require an insulating section to prevent a different potential being introduced into the installation. Where doubt exists about whether the part in question is an extraneous-conductive-part or not, it should be verified by test, see Section 6.

Protective bonding minimum sizes

Section 544 of BS 7671 contains the requirements for protective bonding generally, with Regulation 544.1.1 giving the requirements for the sizing of the main protective bonding conductors. Inspectors will need to verify conductor size as part of the inspection process and will need to be aware that different sizes are required for different systems.

Sizing for TN-S & TT supplies

The main protective bonding conductors for TN-S and TT supplies shall have a csa not less than half the csa required for the Earthing conductor of the installation and must not be less than 6 mm^2 in any case, see Table 3.8.

Table 3.8 Protective bonding sizes for TN-S and TT supplies		
TN-S and TT supplies		
csa of Line conductor mm^2	**csa of Earthing conductor mm^2**	**csa of Protective bonding conductor mm^2**
16	16	10
25	16	10
35	16	10
50	25	16
70	35	25*
ˣThe csa need not exceed 25 mm^2 If copper or equivalent conductance		

Sizing for PME supplies

The minimum csa for main protective bonding conductors for PME supplies shall be selected in accordance with BS 7671 Table 54.8, summarised in Table 3.9.

PME protective bonding is sized in relation to the PEN conductor and can result in larger conductors being required. This is to stop overheating of such conductors during an open-circuit fault to the PEN conductor.

Table 3.9 TN-C-S (PME) Protective bonding conductor sizes

Copper equivalent csa of the PEN conductor	csa of Protective bonding conductor
35 or less	10
over 35 up to 50	16
over 50 up to 95	25
over 95 up to 150	35
over 150	50

Supplementary protective equipotential bonding

Supplementary bonding is considered to be an addition to fault protection and therefore is subject to the requirements of BS 7671 Regulation 415.2 Additional Protection. Supplementary bonding is carried out to reduce touch voltages between exposed-conductive-parts and extraneous-conductive-parts within a whole installation, part of an installation, a location, or an item of equipment.

Supplementary bonding may be used for a number of reasons, such as:

- Where automatic disconnection is not achievable
- Areas of increased risk
- Rooms containing a bath or shower (Section 701)
- Swimming pools (Section 702)
- Agricultural and horticultural installations (Section 705)
- Medical locations (Section 710)
- Fairgrounds, amusement parks and circuses (Section 740)

Supplementary bonding conductor

Regulation 544.2 sets out the requirements for supplementary bonding conductors; there are subtle differences depending on what equipment or services are being connected. Where no mechanical protection is provided, the minimum size of the conductor needs to be at least 4.0 mm^2.

Locations containing a bath or shower

Installations carried out during the 16th Edition to the Wiring Regulations almost certainly included supplementary bonding in any locations containing a bath or shower. Fortunately, with the introduction of the 17th Edition in 2008, supplementary bonding could be omitted under certain circumstances.

It is important to understand the various requirements introduced over the years because it is likely that a mixture of installation practices will be found in older properties.

The first half of Regulation 701.415.2 concerns the practice of supplementary protective equipotential bonding. The second half of Regulation 701.415.2 states that where the location containing a bath or shower is in a building in which protective equipotential bonding has been carried out in accordance with Regulation 411.3.1.2, supplementary bonding may be omitted where all three of the following conditions are met:

- All final circuits must comply with the requirements for automatic disconnection of supply according to Regulation 411.3.2
- All final circuits must be provided with additional protection by means of a 30 mA RCD
- All extraneous-conductive-parts of the location are effectively connected to the protective equipotential bonding as per Regulation 411.3.1.2

When conducting EICRs where 30 mA RCDs have been used for additional protection, it is important to check that these requirements have been met in order to dismiss the need for supplementary bonding.

If an item of metalwork within a location containing a bath or shower does not come within the definition of an extraneous-conductive-part due, for example, to plastic inserts, then the metalwork does not need to be supplementary bonded. It is effectively isolated metalwork.

See Fig 3.18 illustrates a typical bathroom with supplementary bonding.

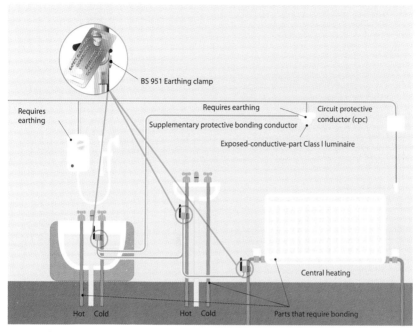

BS 951 Earthing clamp

Requires
earthing

Requires earthing

Circuit protective
conductor (cpc)

Supplementary protective bonding conductor

Exposed-conductive-part Class I luminaire

Central heating

Hot   Cold

Hot   Cold

Parts that require bonding

Fig 3.18 illustrates a typical bathroom with supplementary bonding

3.3 Automatic disconnection of supply (ADS)

The requirements for ADS can be found in Chapter 41 of BS 7671, in general, there are two aspects involved with this protective measure:

1. Basic protection is used to prevent contact with live parts, and

2. Fault protection is provided by the protective earthing system and automatic disconnection in case of a fault

Fault to Earth

Fig 3.19 relates to TN systems and shows the path of the earth fault current in the event of a line to Earth fault in one of the circuits. For clarity, only one circuit is shown, and it supplies a load with a metal casing that is connected to Earth via the cpc. The example shown is for a TN-S earthing system.

The direction of the earth fault current path is indicated by the arrows. It will be observed that the fault current flows in a loop. It returns back to the supply transformer via the protective conductors, then goes through the winding of the transformer and returns to the fault within the installation via the line conductor. For TT systems, refer to Fig 3.20 where the mass of

Earth between the installation and the origin forms part of the earth fault current path.

The resistance met by the fault current is known as impedance, due to the presence of the transformer winding in the path, and the symbol for impedance is Z. This fault path is called the earth fault loop impedance and is abbreviated to Z_s.

The unit of impedance is the same as the unit of resistance, which is an ohm. The intention is that the fault current will be high enough to disconnect the overcurrent protective device within the required time, known as the disconnection time.

The value of the earth fault current is directly related to the value of operating voltage and earth fault loop impedance, known simply as Ohms law.

Therefore, the lower the value of Z_s, the higher the value of the earth fault current, and the quicker it will operate the protective device in order to disconnect the faulty circuit.

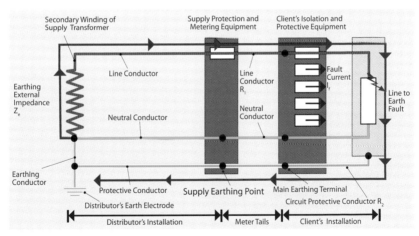

Fig 3.19 TN-S system Earth fault current path in a standard circuit

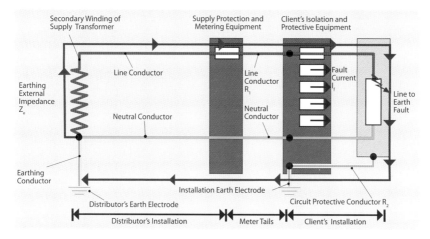

Fig 3.20 TT system Earth fault current path in a standard circuit

The earth fault loop impedance (Zs)

Reference to Figs 3.19 and 3.20, illustrates that the path of the earth fault current is composed of two parts:

- The external part (this is, the part external to the premises) and
- The internal part (i.e. the part within the premises)

Therefore, the impedance of the earth fault current Z_s is also composed of these two parts. The external part is called Z_e, and the internal part is called $(R_1 + R_2)$.

Z_s is measured simply by means of a commonly available earth fault loop impedance tester. In order to ascertain whether the reading of Z_s obtained is acceptable, an understanding of the maximum permitted values of Z_s is required. This includes understanding the need for disconnection times. The formula for the earth fault loop impedance is as follows:
$$Z_s = Z_e + (R_1 + R_2)$$

Where:
Z_e = the external impedance
R_1 = the resistance of the line conductor
R_2 = the resistance of the circuit protective conductor
Z_s = the earth fault loop impedance

Disconnection times

As the severity of an electric shock depends not only on the value of the current flowing but also upon the time that the current flows, BS 7671 quotes the maximum disconnection times for each type and rating of overcurrent protective device. This means that the protective device of the circuit must operate to disconnect the electricity supply within these times in the event of a fault to Earth.

Regulation 411.3.2.2 states that disconnection times in Table 41.1, found in BS 7671, shall be applied to final circuits with a rated current not exceeding:

- 63 A with one or more socket-outlets, and
- 32 A supplying only fixed connected current-using equipment

The disconnection times for 230 V AC final circuits, found in Table 41.1 are:

- 0.4 s for TN systems
- 0.2 s for TT systems

Where disconnection is achieved in a TT system by an overcurrent protective device and protective equipotential bonding of all extraneous-conductive-parts, in accordance with Regulation 411.3.1.2, the maximum disconnection times for TN systems may be used.

In distribution circuits, i.e., sub-mains, and for final circuits not covered by Regulation 411.3.2.2, table 41.1 does not apply. In TN systems, the disconnection time must not exceed 5 s, and in TT systems, the disconnection time must not exceed 1 s. (see Regulations 411.3.2.3 and 411.3.2.4).

Maximum Z_s values are given in BS 7671, Tables 41.2, 41.3, and 41.4. The headings of these tables must be carefully noted to understand how each Table is to be used. When the earth fault loop impedance, Z_s, is measured using an earth fault loop impedance tester, the reading obtained must be less than the relevant maximum value of Z_s in the appropriate Table.

Z$_s$ corrected for temperature

It should be noted that BS 7671 Tables 41.2, 41.3, and 41.4 all have a similar note at the end of the Table. This note states that the maximum impedance given in the Table should not be exceeded if the impedance is measured when the circuit conductors are at their maximum operating temperature (i.e., 70°C). Usually, the circuit conductors will be at much less than this when testing is carried out. They may be assumed to be 20°C. Values taken at 20°C can be corrected to 70°C for 70°C cables by multiplying the maximum value of Z$_s$ by 0.8, as stated in Appendix 3 of BS 7671.

Maximum Z$_s$ figures for commonly used devices, corrected for temperature, are produced earlier in this Section (Table 3.3) and in Appendix 2 of this guide.

For TT Earthing systems, RCDs are often used to provide fault protection. This is mainly due to the fact that earth electrode resistance is too excessive to meet the maximum earth fault loop impedance requirements for the circuit's protective device. Table 41.5 of BS 7671 lists the maximum earth fault loop impedance values to ensure effective RCD operation, as summarised in Table 3.5. It is important that the electrode resistance remains stable and, therefore, should be as low as practicable (under 200 Ω is deemed satisfactory).

3.4 Protection by SELV, PELV or Electrical Separation

Electrical Separation

The requirements for electrical separation can be found in Section 413 of BS 7671. In general, there are two aspects involved with this protective measure:

1. Basic protection is used to prevent contact with live parts, and

2. Fault protection is provided by simple separation, where the circuit is separated from other circuits and from Earth.

Electrical separation is usually limited to one item of equipment only, where the requirements listed in Regulation 413.1.1 for electrical separation are fulfilled if live parts are insulated by basic insulation, barriers or enclosures (basic protection), and fault protection is provided by simple separation.

Regulation 722.413.1.2 is an example of where this protective measure is permitted to be used for electric vehicle charging installations, allowing the supply to one electric vehicle from one unearthed source. The circuit must be supplied through a fixed isolating transformer complying with BS EN 61558-2-4. Fig 3.21 shows there is no connection to Earth on the secondary winding of the transformer, and therefore the earth fault loop path is broken, removing any potential shock hazard.

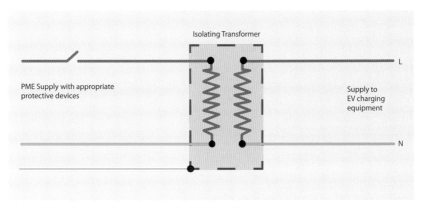

Fig 3.21 Isolating transformer supplying EV charging equipment

SELV (Separated Extra-low Voltage) and PELV (Protective Extra-low Voltage

The requirements for using the protective measure of extra-low voltage provided by SELV or PELV can be found in Section 414 of BS 7671. In general, protection by extra-low voltage by SELV or PELV requires:

- Voltage to be limited to the upper limit of voltage band I (50 V AC or 120 V DC), and

- Protective separation between SELV or PELV systems from other circuits which are not SELV or PELV, and

- Basic insulation between SELV or PELV systems and other SELV or PELV systems, and

- Basic insulation between SELV systems and Earth (this requirement is not applicable to PELV systems)

Most requirements are the same for both systems; the main difference is that PELV is not electrically separated from Earth, but otherwise satisfies all the requirements of a SELV system.

Section 4
Safe Isolation of Electrical Supplies

4.0 Safe Isolation of Electrical Supplies

4.1 Legislation and Regulations

It is a legal requirement that employers must ensure that their employees working on electrical equipment are competent to do so. Employees must be trained and instructed in the implementation of safe systems of work. This may involve the issue of written procedures, work permits, and instructions on the use of locking-off devices, warning notices, approved voltage indicating devices, and voltage proving unit.

Legislation
The following documents cover safe isolation procedures and limit the activities to electrical installations operating at up to 1000 V AC.

The Health and Safety at Work Act 1974 sets out the general health and safety duties of employers, employees, and the self-employed. Under this Act, employees are required to co-operate with their employer to enable these requirements to be met. This includes any instruction given on safe systems of work.

The Electricity at Work Regulations 1989, require that precautions shall be taken against the risk of death or personal injury from work on or near electrical systems.

The Management of Health and Safety at Work Regulations 1999 requires employers to make suitable and sufficient assessment of risk to the health and safety of their employees and other persons, arising out of, or in connection with, their conduct and their undertakings. When a company has five or more persons who are employed, the employer must record the significant findings of risk assessment.

HSE Guidance
Guidance on devising staff working practices for work on electrical equipment can be found in a booklet entitled, Electricity at Work, Safe Working Practices (HSG 85), produced by the Health and Safety Executive.

Electricity at Work Regulations
The Electricity at Work Regulations are covered in detail in Section 1.2 of this guide. However, the following Regulations are important with regards to safe isolation:

Regulation 12

A means of isolation must be provided for all electrical equipment. Circuits may be isolated in groups, provided that there is no need for other circuits in the group to remain energized when one needs to be isolated.

Regulation 13

Precautions need to be taken on equipment that has been made dead. This includes securing the means of disconnection in the off position, putting a warning/caution notice or label at the point of work.

Regulation 14

Dead working should be the normal method of carrying out work on electrical equipment or circuits. Live working should be carried out only in particular circumstances where it is unreasonable to work dead.

Regulation 14, states that no person shall be engaged in any work activity on or so near any live conductor – other than one suitably covered with insulation material so as to prevent danger – that danger may arise unless:

- It is unreasonable in all the circumstances for it to be dead

And

- It is reasonable in all circumstances for him/her to be at work on or near it while it is live

And

- Suitable precautions, including where necessary the provision of suitable protective equipment, are taken to prevent injury

Remember that all the above conditions must be met for work on live conductors to be carried out.

4.2 Hidden dangers

When inspecting and testing unfamiliar installations, care must be taken as this type of work can be particularly hazardous for a number of reasons which may include, circuit identification not being available, or being incorrectly identified.

The practice of making use of the neutral of one circuit 'borrowed neutrals', for use on another is not permitted by BS 7671, Section 314. You may come across borrowed neutrals on lighting circuits, for example, on two-way lighting which has been put on separate circuits, see Fig 4.1.

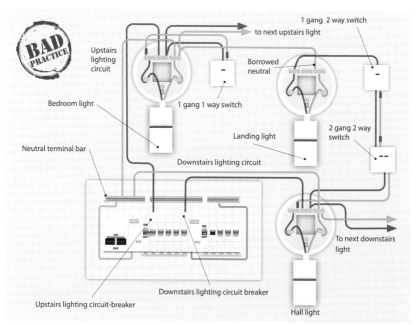

Fig 4.1 Shared (borrowed) neutral in lighting circuits

Any circuit installed must be treated with caution, proven to be isolated and de-energized prior to work starting. Extreme care must be taken when cutting cables, especially single core conductors in conduit/trunking or screened/armoured cables.

The main purpose of safe isolation is that the point of isolation should be under the control of the person who is going to carry out the work on the isolated circuit or equipment. There are several ways of achieving safe isolations which depend on the type of:

- Distribution Equipment/Boards and Consumer Units supplying the circuit
- Overcurrent device used to protect the circuit
- Local Isolation for equipment

It is important to ensure that the correct point of isolation is identified, and an appropriate means of isolation used, which ensures the supply cannot inadvertently be re-energised.

Isolation Points

Suitable points of isolation of fixed equipment can be a plug and socket-outlet, switched fused connection unit, multi-pole isolating switch, circuit-breaker or fuse, see examples in Fig 4.2.

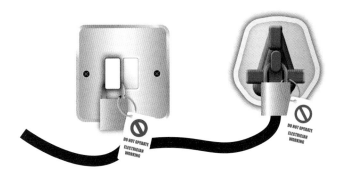

Fig 4.2 Examples of Isolation systems

4.3 Isolating a complete installation

The isolation of circuits and equipment using the main switch or double-pole switch disconnector is the preferred method. The device is locked off, using a lock which has a non-interchangeable key, or a combination lock, where the combination is known only to the person carrying out the work.

Some consumer units and distribution boards have lockable covers and are supplied with a key, but are only suitable if a unique key, as illustrated in Fig 4.3. Others have a lockable facility where a separate padlock is required to lock it.

Fig 4.3 Example of lockable Distribution Board/Consumer Unit

When replacing an existing consumer unit, distribution board or main switchgear, it is necessary for the incoming meter tails supplied from the supplier's meter to be disconnected. This involves the distributor's service intake fuse being withdrawn off load to achieve isolation. Remember, in legal terms, this service fuse can only be withdrawn by the distributor, or by those organisations the distributor has authorised to carry out such work.

Isolation of individual circuits

When it is not practical to isolate a consumer unit or distribution board, an individual circuit fed from it may be isolated, depending on the type of protection device used. When a circuit-breaker has been used it should be locked-off using an appropriate locking-off device with an appropriate padlock having a non-interchangeable key which is retained by the person carrying out the work, as illustrated in Fig 4.4.

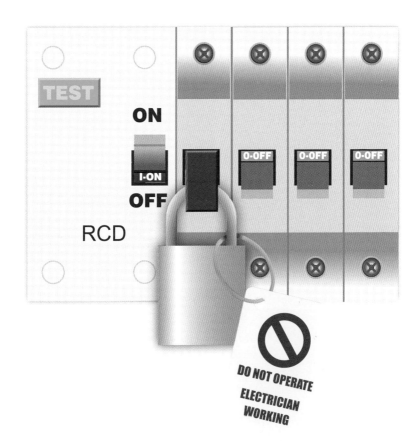

Fig 4.4 Example of a lockable device for individual circuit isolation

If a fuse has been used for the protection of an individual circuit, removing the fuse, keeping it in a safe place only accessible to the person carrying out the work is acceptable. In order to prevent another fuse being inserted, a lockable fuse insert with a padlock should be used.

4.4 Safe isolation procedure

Before any electrical work is carried out, it should be confirmed that the installation is safe to work on. Part of being safe to work on is the need for the installation to be isolated at the points that are under inspection, maintenance or installation.

In the case of EICRs, the safe isolation of electrical supplies refers to those inspections and any testing that could expose the inspector/tester to hazardous voltages.

Safe isolation is not just the isolation of a whole installation, it can be for an individual circuit or particular distribution board (DB) or consumer unit (CU).

Although safe isolation is a standard procedure, it can have slightly different processes for domestic or commercial/industrial installations.

A domestic safe isolation procedure may have only one CU to deal with, which may make things simpler, whereas in commercial and industrial scenarios, there may well be multiple DBs.

Having multiple DBs or CUs to deal with, will mean that the inspector will need to be more vigilant. In all cases, proprietary lock off kits should be used to ensure that operatives are safe when coming into contact with equipment, which would normally have voltages present.

Remember that when we mention the 'electrical supply,' this may also be an individual circuit, DB, or CU, not just the whole installation.

It is important that any safe isolation system follows a pre-determined and risk assessed process. The following safe isolation procedures are ideal for general use and take into account the differing requirements for a domestic procedure, see Fig 4.5, and an industrial or commercial procedure, see Fig 4.6. These safe isolation procedures are also reproduced in Appendix 2 of this Guide for ease of use.

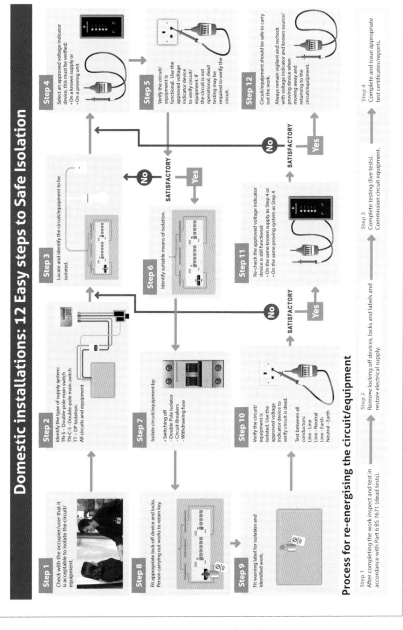

Domestic installations: 12 Easy steps to Safe Isolation

Step 1
Check with the occupier/user that it is acceptable to isolate the circuit/equipment.

Step 2
Identify the type of supply system:
TN-S – Double-pole main switch
TN-C-S – Double-pole main switch
TT – DP Isolation.
All circuits and equipment

Step 3
Locate and identify the circuit/equipment to be isolated.

Step 4
Select an approved voltage indicator device, this must be verified:
- On a known supply or
- On a proving unit

Step 5
Verify the circuit/equipment is functional. Use the approved voltage indicator device to verify the circuit/equipment. If the circuit is not operational, dead testing may be required to verify the circuit.

Step 6
Identify suitable means of isolation.

Step 7
Isolate circuit/equipment by:
- Switching off
- Double Pole Isolator
- Circuit-Breakers
- Withdrawing fuse

Step 8
Fit appropriate lock-off device and locks. Person carrying out works to retain key.

Step 9
Fit warning label for isolation and identified work.

Step 10
Verify the circuit/equipment is isolated. Use the approved voltage indicator device to verify circuit is dead.
Test between all conductors:
Line - Line
Line - Neutral
Line - Earth
Neutral - Earth

Step 11
Re-check the approved voltage indicator device is still functional:
- On the same known supply as Step 4 or
- On the same proving system as Step 4

Step 12
Circuit/equipment should be safe to carry out the work.
Always remain vigilant and recheck with voltage indicator and known source/proving device when moving away and returning to the circuit/equipment.

SATISFACTORY No Yes

SATISFACTORY No Yes

Process for re-energising the circuit/equipment

Step 1
After completing the work inspect and test in accordance with Part 6 BS 7671 (dead tests).

Step 2
Remove locking off devices, locks and labels and restore electrical supply.

Step 3
Complete testing (live tests).
Commission circuit equipment.

Step 4
Complete and issue appropriate test certificates/reports.

Fig 4.5 12 easy steps to safe isolation

Industrial and Commercial Installations: 12 Easy steps to Safe Isolation

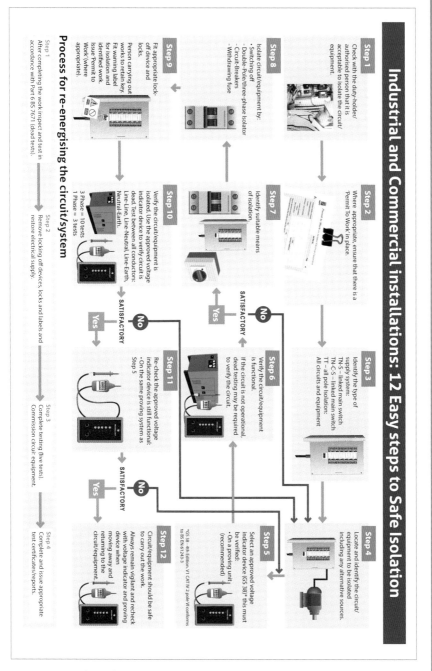

Step 1
Check with the duty-holder/authorised person that it is acceptable to isolate the circuit/equipment.

Step 2
Where appropriate, ensure that there is a 'Permit To Work' in place.

Step 3
Identify the type of supply system:
TN-S – linked main switch
TN-C-S – linked main switch
TT – all pole isolation:
All circuits and equipment

Step 4
Locate and identify the circuit/equipment to be isolated including any alternative sources.

Step 8
Isolate circuit/equipment by:
• Switching off
• Double-Pole/three-phase isolator
• Circuit-Breakers
• Withdrawing fuse

Step 7
Identify suitable means of isolation.

SATISFACTORY → Yes

Step 6
Verify the circuit/equipment is operational.
If the circuit is not operational, dead testing may be required to verify the circuit.

No → SATISFACTORY

Step 5
Select an approved voltage indicator device (GS 38)* this must be verified:
• On a proving unit/(recommended)

*GS 38 - 4th Edition. VI CAT IV 2 pole VI conforms to BS EN 61243-3

Step 9
Fit appropriate lock-off device and locks.

Step 10
Verify the circuit/equipment is isolated. Use the approved voltage indicator device to verify circuit is dead. Test between all conductors:
Line-Line, Line-Neutral, Line-Earth, Neutral-Earth.
3 Phase = 10 tests
1 Phase = 3 tests

SATISFACTORY → Yes

Step 11
Re-check the approved voltage indicator device is still functional:
• On the same proving system as Step 5

Yes → SATISFACTORY

Step 12
Circuit/equipment should be safe to carry out the work.
Always remain vigilant and recheck device when moving away and returning to the circuit/equipment.

Process for re-energising the circuit/system

Step 1
After completing the work inspect and test in accordance with Part 6 BS 7671 (dead tests).

Step 1
After completing the work inspect and test in accordance with Part 6 BS 7671 (dead tests).

Step 2
Remove locking off devices, locks and labels and restore electrical supply.

Step 2
Complete testing (five tests). Commission circuit equipment.

Step 3
Complete testing (five tests). Commission circuit equipment.

Step 4
Complete and issue appropriate test certificates/reports.

Fig 4.6 Industrial and Commercial Installations 12 easy steps to safe isolation

99

Permits to Work

On High Voltage Systems an electrical permit-to-work system must be used for work to start on the systems which have been made dead. The system can also be useful for certain LV work, especially in large factories or production plants. The permit to work is primarily a statement that a circuit or item of equipment is isolated and safe to work on. You are likely to also require a risk assessment and method statements for this process.

Proving that Isolated Circuits and Equipment are Dead

Before proving a circuit or equipment has been isolated, you should first confirm that it was live and operational. After the isolation of a circuit or equipment has taken place and before you start work, you should prove that the parts you are about to work on are dead. Remember, never assume that a circuit or equipment is dead because you believe that you have correctly identified and isolated the relevant circuit or equipment.

The correct procedure for proving that a circuit or item of equipment is dead is to use a propriety test lamp or two-pole voltage indicator constructed to the standard stated in HSE Guidance Note GS 38, explained in Section 1.

Where proprietary test lamps or two-pole voltage indicators are used, they should always be proved to be working on a known live source of supply or proprietary proving unit before and after use, see Fig 4.7.

Remember all conductors of a circuit, including the neutral, should be tested and proved dead before starting work.

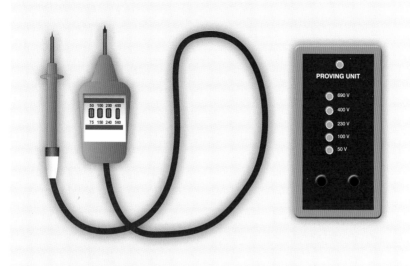

Fig 4.7 Proprietary test lamps (left) and Voltage Proving Unit (right)

Dangers on TT Supply Systems

When the supply forms part of a TT system, the incoming neutral cannot reliably be regarded as being at earth potential. Therefore, in this case, a multi-pole switching device disconnecting the line, and neutral conductors must always be used as a means of isolation. For similar reasons, all poles of the supply must be disconnected. It can, therefore, be seen that single-pole isolation using single-pole circuit-breakers or fuses is not acceptable.

Warning Notice

Where there is any risk that an isolated electrical supply to an installation, circuit or piece of equipment could be reinstated, an appropriate warning notice should be placed at the point of isolation, and an example is illustrated in Fig 4.8. It is good practice to use a warning notice at all times.

Fig 4.8 Safe isolation warning notice

4.6 Isolation of larger installations

For larger installations, such as those found in a factory where several tradespersons may be involved with work on an installation and its connected equipment. In these scenarios, multiple isolations may be required. Best practice in this instance is to use a multi-lock hasp, allowing each tradesperson to fit their own lock to prevent access to the main isolator. This will ensure the system remains isolated until all persons working on the system have completed their particular work activity and removed their locks from the hasp, see Fig 4.9.

Fig 4.9 Multiple isolation hasp

Isolation Requirements Where More Than One CU/DB is Installed

The general requirements for isolation and switching are found in Chapter 46 and Section 537 of BS 7671.

Regulation 462.1 requires that each electrical installation be provided with a means of isolation from the supply, or supplies, and Regulation 462.1.201 requires a linked main switch or CB as near to the origin of every installation, as is practicable, to switch the on-load supply for isolation purposes.

From an inspection point of view, where there is more than one consumer unit or distribution board installed in the same building. Does this require a check to see that there is a main isolating switch to allow all consumer units/distribution boards to be isolated simultaneously?

The references to, 'each installation' and, 'every installation' in these Regulations means we must clarify what exactly is meant by an electrical installation. For example, is the additional consumer unit and the circuit(s) supplied by it, part of the main installation or is it counted as a second installation?

An electrical installation (which can be abbreviated to 'Installation') is defined in Part 2, Definitions of BS 7671 as follows:

'An assembly of associated electrical equipment having coordinated characteristics to fulfil specific purposes'. By this definition, an electrical installation can be considered to include a domestic consumer unit and the final circuits supplied by it.

Likewise, an additional consumer unit provided for a specific purpose, such as supplying an electric shower, or a building extension, can also be considered to be an electrical installation. Therefore premises, including domestic premises, can have more than one electrical installation, but each installation must have its own means of disconnection from the supply, which must be located as near as practicable to the origin of the installation.

Regulation 514.11.1 requires that each device used for isolation must be clearly identified to avoid confusion, see example label.

Main switch label

Isolation Arrangements at the Origin

In accordance with Regulation 461.2, in TN-S or TN-C-S systems, the neutral conductor need not be isolated or switched where it can be regarded as being reliably connected to Earth by suitably low impedance. This is the case where electricity supplies are provided in accordance with the Electricity Safety, Quality and Continuity Regulations. This generally applies to single-phase and three-phase supplies at the origin and throughout the installation. However, an exception is made for the origin of domestic or similar installations. In TT systems, the neutral conductor must be capable of being isolated or switched at the origin and throughout the installation.

The reason that the neutral conductor need not be isolated or switched in TN-S or TN-C-S systems is that, in normal operating conditions, the potential of the neutral conductor will be close to that of exposed and extraneous-conductive-parts within the equipotential zone. This is because they are connected to Earth, and the risk of any hazard occurring due to solid neutral is minimal. That being said, a small potential between the neutral conductor and Earth is likely to be present and may be capable of giving a perceived electric shock.

Where the neutral conductor has not been included in the means of isolation or switching in TN-S and TN-C-S systems, provision must be made for disconnecting the neutral conductor. This could be a bolted link, accessible to skilled persons only and incapable of being removed except by means of a tool. This gives skilled persons the option of disconnecting the neutral if they deem it necessary due to the nature of the work. During this process, it is advisable to install a warning label to ensure the reconnection of the removed neutral link.

Isolation Arrangements at the Origin of Single-phase Systems

The main switch, or linked circuit-breaker, must interrupt the live conductors, e.g., the line and neutral conductors of a single-phase supply, regardless of the type of supply system.

This requires a double-pole main switch in domestic consumer units. While the Regulations don't encourage unskilled people to carry out electrical work, it is generally accepted that unskilled people may carry out work on the electrical installation unaware of the potential which can exist between neutral and Earth. This requirement to interrupt the line and neutral conductors applies only to the main switch in domestic premises.

Fig 4.10 shows the arrangement at the origin where the main switch is intended for operation by ordinary persons (e.g. in domestic premises).

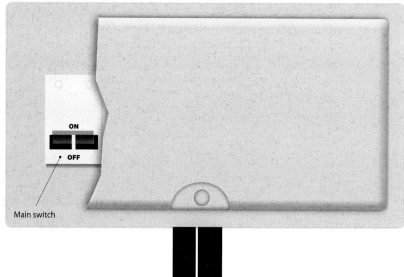

Main switch

Fig 4.10 Main isolation switch

Isolation Arrangements at the Origin of Three-phase Systems

In three-phase systems, there is no difference in the arrangement at the origin where access is restricted to skilled or instructed people only, or where the main switch is intended for operation by ordinary persons.

Single-phase and three-phase TT systems

In TT systems, the neutral conductor must be capable of being isolated or switched at the origin and throughout the installation. In single-phase and three-phase TT systems, there is no difference in the arrangement at the origin where access is restricted to skilled or instructed persons only, or where the main switch is intended for operation by ordinary persons.

Section 5

Test instruments

5.0 Test instruments

5.1 Voltage tester

When we talk about a 'voltage tester' from a BS 7671 inspection and testing perspective, we refer to a device that falls within the remit and production standards contained within HSE GS 38, see Section 2 of this guide, that being BS EN 61243-3 for voltage testers.

A voltage tester for carrying out electrical installation tests to BS 7671, needs to accurately measure, and then accurately indicate to the operator, the presence of a known or expected voltage, which may or may not be present in the circuit or equipment under test. We then need to confirm that test equipment is operating correctly by referencing it against a known supply of similar voltage, which in general terms is seen as a confirmation check box or voltage proving unit, see Fig 5.5.

Acceptable Voltage Testers generally fall into two categories, both of which are two pole:

- Voltage indicator type:

Voltage indicators see Fig 5.1, as the name suggests, indicate when a voltage is present, by displaying it numerically on a display screen.

- Lamp indicator type:

Lamp indicators see Fig 5.2, as the name suggests, indicate when voltage is present by displaying it visually in the form of a series of lamps, which indicate which voltage range is present.

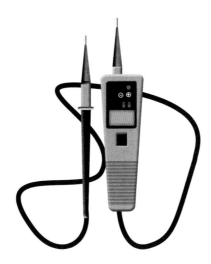

Fig 5.1 Voltage numeric indicator tester

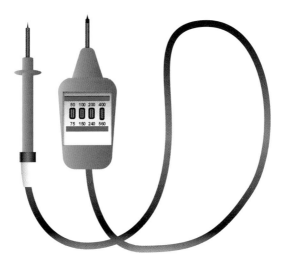

Fig 5.2 Voltage visual lamp indicator

Either device can be used and in some cases the voltage indicator type of devices, may be incorporated into a Multi-Function Tester (MFT), which is covered later in this Section. Some modern devices often incorporate both lamp and voltage indicator types in a combined device, see Fig 5.3

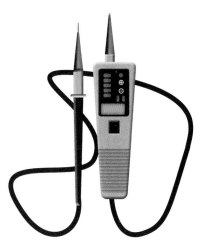

Fig 5.3 Combined Test lamp and voltage Indicator tester

Warning

Not all voltage indicating devices should be used to confirm the presence of voltage for BS 7671 testing purposes. The following is a list of those devices that are known to be unstable and should only be used as part of a fault-finding process, prior to accurate voltage confirmation, and prior to any significant testing.

- Voltage indicator stick
- Multi-meter (not to be confused with an MFT)
- Neon Screwdriver, see Fig 5.4

Fig 5.4 Neon test screwdriver

5.1.1 Voltage tester confirmation check box (proving unit)

Voltage tester confirmation, or check box, proving units, see Fig 5.5 as the name suggests, are self-contained and powered devices, that can accurately and consistently replicate a given output voltage. This known and consistent output voltage can be used as a datum, or reference point to check the operation of voltage testers.

When checking appropriate voltage testers, the correct sequence to ensure compliance is as follows:

Step 1   **Check voltage tester against known reference or check box:**
To confirm voltage tester operates correctly at a given voltage.

Step 2   **Use tester to check/measure/confirm state of a circuit in question:**
Test circuit or equipment straight after Step 1.

Step 3   **Re-check voltage tester against the check box:**
This will confirm the voltage tester is working within parameters and wasn't damaged during use, and therefore possible not giving an accurate reading. This step must follow straight after Step 2, with no appreciable delay.

Fig 5.5 Voltage check box/Proving Unit

5.2 Low resistance ohmmeter/Insulation resistance meter

Possibly one of the most often used and essential pieces of equipment, the Low Resistance Ohmmeter is used to gather or confirm three critical pieces of information.

As most single test instruments have a dual use, based on the same general test parameters, the Low Resistance Ohmmeter is used for the following three tests:

1. **Conductor resistance** – Measurement of resistance in conductors, to assess their resistance to current flow

2. **Conductor continuity** – Measurement of resistance in conductors, or enclosures, to confirm continuity and csa throughout their length

3. **Insulation resistance** – Measurement of resistance in conductors, to confirm the state of a conductor's insulation and ability to resist the leakage of voltage.

5.2.1 Conductor resistance (Low resistance ohmmeter)

Arguably one of the most important tests we carry out is the measurement of a conductor's resistance to current flow. It forms the basis of our calculations for current carrying capacity and is key to determining the maximum resistance in an overall circuit (Z_s). It is the understanding and knowledge of the Z_s of a circuit, which allows us to specify the correct OCPD, taking account of its operating time characteristics and those required for a given circuit.

Resistance values for measuring continuity of conductors are given in Ohms (Ω). A Low ohmmeter configured for conductor resistance measurement can be seen in Fig 5.6.

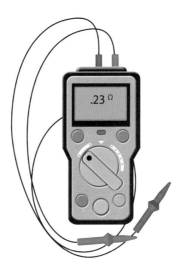

Fig 5.6 Low ohmmeter configured for conductor resistance measurement

5.2.2 Conductor continuity (Low resistance ohmmeter)

The ability to understand if a conductor, is continuous throughout its length, and has a consistent csa consummate with its length, is a requirement of Regulation 643.2.

As well as conductors, the continuity of enclosures, conduits, and trunking could require measurement in some cases, to confirm they have continuity, see Regulation 543.22. This is especially relevant where their construction forms the protective conductor of a circuit or group of circuits.

Last but by no means least, we need to confirm the continuity of connections to various terminals where they form part of extraneous-conductive-parts, and/or exposed-conductive-parts, where there is a requirement for them to be bonded. This test will also highlight high resistance joints, caused by damaged, loose or corroded connections.

Resistance values for the measuring of continuity of conductors, enclosures, or connections are given in Ohms (Ω). A Low ohmmeter configured for conductor continuity measurement can be seen in Fig 5.7.

Fig 5.7 Low ohmmeter configured for continuity measurement

5.2.3 Insulation resistance (Low resistance ohmmeter)

During construction of an installation and its initial verification stage, the state of the insulation resistance can highlight possible damage. Where damage has occurred during the installation process, it must be repaired prior to energizing.

From a Periodic Inspection perspective, an insulation resistance test is possibly the most important we can evaluate. Knowing and understanding the state of a conductor's insulation material is vital.

When the insulation material, surrounding a conductor, starts to degrade or is damaged in some way, stray voltages can leak from the conductor, to surrounding exposed conductive parts, or to other conductors. These leakages can cause either electric shocks or fires, depending on the severity and location of the insulation breakdown.

Resistance values for measuring a conductor's insulation resistance are given in Mega Ohms/Megohms (MΩ). A Low ohmmeter configured for insulation resistance measurement can be seen in Fig 5.8.

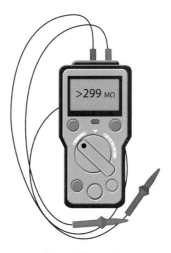

Fig 5.8 Low ohmmeter configured for insulation resistance measurement

5.3 Earth fault loop impedance (EFLI) tester

When an installation or circuit under test is live, we need to confirm the potential fault path to earth, under fault conditions.

A circuit's earth fault path is known as it's loop, and we can only measure this value when the circuit is energized. We need to know this value, as it gives us the overall resistance of the internal fault path combined with the external fault path.

As this measurement is a resistance measurement, it is given in ohms (Ω); however, as the measurement is carried out on a live circuit, we refer to it as an 'impedance' value.

Impedance is the ability of a conductor to impede, or resist current flow, in a live circuit, and is referred to as Z.

In an electrical installation, we have two possible impedance values:

- Z_e – The external value of resistance for the earth fault loop path.
- Z_s – The combined external and internal values of resistance for the earth fault loop path, where the internal value of resistance for the earth fault path, is taken as the R_1+R_2 value of a circuit.

It is possible to calculate Z_s, without direct live measurement, see Section 6 of this guide; however, it is seen as unreliable, as it may not take account of weaknesses in a circuit, once energized. Calculated Z_s is notoriously higher than the measured value of Z_s, due to naturally occurring parallel earth paths that can be present in an installation.

A parallel earth path can be anything from a metal back box being in contact with the building, or an earth fly lead if fitted, to a utility with protective bonding, whose pipework is then in contact with the installation's building structure. Known as fortuitous earths, these can significantly affect the Z_s of a circuit, and it is, for this reason, the actual measured value of Z_s is ordinarily used instead of the calculated.

Earth fault loop impedance (EFLI) testers come in different configurations, some requiring two leads to take a reading see Fig 5.9, and some requiring three leads to take a reading see Fig 5.10.

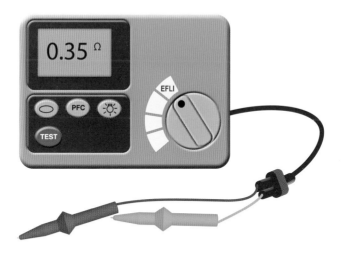

Fig 5.9 Two lead EFLI tester

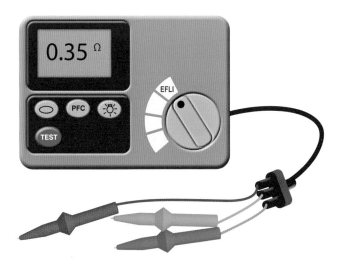

Fig 5.10 Three lead EFLI tester

Most modern meters will also have the ability to test with RCDs or RCBOs in circuit, using a special no-trip setting. This is needed as the magnitude of the test current used to take the reading can cause RCDs to trip, so a reduced magnitude test is required for testing where an RCD is present, see Fig 5.11.

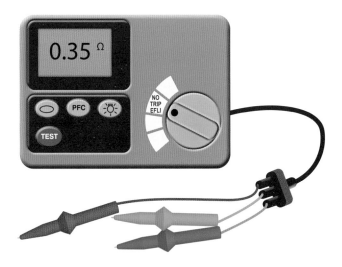

Fig 5.11 EFLI tester set to no-trip test with an RCD in circuit.

5.4 Prospective Fault Current (I_{pf}) tester

The prospective fault current (I_{pf}) is the highest expected current that can flow in a given conductor, circuit or installation under fault conditions. The magnitude of any prospective fault current is governed by the resistance of the conductor(s) in a given circuit and the applied voltage.

There are two possible prospective fault current values, depending on where the measurement is taken from:

- **Prospective short-circuit current (P_{ssc})**
  Taken as a prospective short-circuit in a healthy circuit, between the Line and Neutral conductors, or between Line and Line in a three phase installation.

- **Prospective earth fault current (P_{efc})**
  Taken as a prospective overload caused by a fault in a healthy circuit, between the Line conductors and cpc.

Measurement of the prospective fault current (I_{pf}) is generally taken during the EFLI measurement, as this is the dual role of this particular test instrument. The EFLI test instrument uses a mathematic algorithm, based on ohms law, to calculate the I_{pf}. In this case, the value used or measured, is the P_{efc}, unless the test instrument is specifically configured to measure the P_{ssc}. These two values generally differ based on the resistance of conductors, or fault paths, which are specific to each. The different value used, or taken, will depend on whether the inspector is looking to confirm the current rating of a device in short-circuit overload, or for Earth fault scenarios.

It is possible to calculate the I_{pf} individually, if the resistance or impedance of a circuit is known and the voltage applied to it is also available, as I_{pf} is nothing more than an Ohm's law calculation, see Fig 5.12.

Fig 5.12 Prospective Fault Current I_{pf} (P_{efc}) examples, calculated manually using Ohm's law

Example 1 – I_{pf} in a circuit

Z_s of circuit (Z_e + (R_1+ R_2)) in Ω = 0. 65 Ω

Known voltage (V) applied to circuit = 243 V

Maximum Current (I) that can flow in circuit =? A

$$I \quad = \quad \frac{V}{R}$$

$$I \quad = \quad \frac{243}{0.65}$$

$$I \quad = \quad 374 \text{ A}$$

$$\therefore I_{pf} \quad = \quad 374 \text{ A}$$

Example 2 – I_{pf} of installation

Z_e of installation measured in Ω = 0. 17 Ω

Known installation supply voltage (V) = 253 V

Maximum Current (I) that can flow in installation =? A

$$I \quad = \quad \frac{V}{R}$$

$$I \quad = \quad \frac{253}{0.17}$$

$$I \quad = \quad 1488.24 \text{ A}$$

$$\therefore I_{pf} \quad = \quad 1448 \text{ A}$$

5.5 RCD tester

With ever more emphasis being put on the correct choice of RCDs, based on the equipment in circuit, there is an increasing diversity of equipment designed to test their correct operation.

In its basic form, the RCD tester is used to confirm if the RCD under test conforms with the requirements imposed upon it by BS 7671. Those tests are currently;

- 1 x rated leakage current (for RCDs in excess of 30 mA) maximum value allowed 300 ms (BS EN 61008; 61009) devices.

- 5 x rated leakage current (for RCDs up to 30 mA) maximum value allowed 40 ms

- No-trip at half the rated value (although this is not recorded on BS 7671 model forms)

Note:
These tests should be taken at 0° and 180° of the waveform and the worst-case findings used.

What is often neglected are the types of RCD and their characteristics or sensitivity to DC current present within the circuit they are protecting. The four main types of RCD and their operating restrictions are shown in Table 5.1.

Table 5.1 Types of RCD and their operating restrictions and marking symbols

RCD	Symbol	Examples of type of equipment / load
Type AC		Resistive, Capacitive, Inductive loads generally without any electronic components, typically: • Immersion heater • Oven/Hob with resistive heating elements • Electric shower • Tungsten & halogen lighting
Type A		Single-phase with electronic components, typically: • Single-phase invertors • Class I IT and Multimedia equipment • Power supplies for Class II equipment • Appliances such as a washing machine that is not frequency controlled e.g. DC or universal motor • Lighting controls such as a dimmer switch and home and building electronic systems LED drivers • Induction hobs • Electric Vehicle charging where any smooth DC fault current is less than 6 mA • Electric Vehicle charging in conjunction with RDC-DD **Type A is also suitable for Type AC applications.**
Type F		Frequency controlled equipment / appliances, typically: • Some washing machines, dishwashers and driers e.g. containing synchronous motors* • Some air conditioning controllers using variable frequency speed drives • Electric Vehicle charging in conjunction with RDC-DD **Type F is also suitable for Type AC and Type A applications.**
Type B		Three-phase electronic equipment typically: • Inverters for speed control • UPS • Electric Vehicle charging where any smooth DC fault current is greater than 6 mA • Photovoltaic Power Electronic Converter Systems (PECS) typically: • Industrial machines • Cranes **Type B is also suitable for Type AC, Type A and Type F applications.**

* Manufacturer's instructions should be taken into account.

Power electronic converter PEC
Device or part thereof for the purpose of electronic power conversion, including signalling, measurement, control circuitries and other parts, if essential for the power conversion function

Power electronic converter system PECS
One or more power electronic converters intended to work together with other equipment
For PECS, if a Type B RCD is required, the product will be marked with the symbol ⚠.

The instructions shall include a caution notice highlighting that where an RCD is used for protection against electrical shock, only an RCD of Type B is allowed on the supply side of this product.

When testing an RCD, the test instrument should always be set to the correct type of RCD under test, where that facility is available. If the RCD being tested is a type F, then the RCD test instrument should be set to a type F device, if it has the facility to do so. What this will do, is carry out the RCD test with a pre-determined value of DC current injected into the circuit, see Fig 5.13.

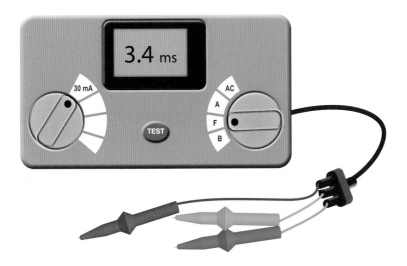

Fig 5.13 RCD test instrument set to evaluate a type F RCD

By confirming that the correct DC current is applied to an RCD during the test, we can determine if it will operate effectively in the presence of any DC leakage current, which may be present during normal operating parameters.

Where the test instrument does not have this facility, it will carry out a basic RCD test, but will not necessarily test the RCDs ability to operate with DC leakage current present.

In addition to the standard tests required by BS 7671, RCD test instruments also have the ability to perform a ramp test. This is where the leakage current injected during the test is gradually increased to the point that the RCD operates. By doing this, the inspector can evaluate the current value in mA, at which the RCD would operate under fault conditions. We can use the ramp test function when fault-finding, or to check an RCDs sensitivity if unwanted tripping was a problem in a circuit or installation.

RCD ramp tests can also be a good indicator of a device's possible damage or end of lifecycle, which can point towards replacement, over a period of time through historic EICRs.

5.6 Phase sequence indicators

As the name suggests, these test instruments are used to confirm that the correct phase rotation has been maintained throughout a poly-phase (three-phase) installation, see Fig 5.14.

Where AC induction motors are in service, for example, it is important to ascertain the correct phase rotation, to ensure that the motor will rotate in the designed direction and as efficiently as possible.

Fig 5.14 Static lamp phase sequence indicator

Correct phase rotation is assumed when the Line conductors are aligned in an installation as they are generated, which is taken to be:

> **L1 - L2 - L3**

Rotation is also taken to be in a clockwise direction.

Phase sequence indicators can be either static lamp display types, see Fig 5.14, or a rotating type, where a disc or similar indicator rotates to indicate the sequence, see Fig 5.15.

Fig 5.15 Rotating disc phase sequence indicator

5.7 Earth electrode resistance tester

Earth electrode resistance or R_a is extremely important to be measured accurately when we are looking to achieve a given disconnection time that is reliable, repeatable, and stable.

There are a number of ways we can do this, but the most effective is to use a dedicated Earth electrode resistance measuring test instrument.

Where we measure the R_a in this way, we call it the *'fall-of-potential method,'* which uses three leads, two as a datum and a third to measure the potential at different points or electrodes. These readings can then be used to calculate the resistance or R_a of the electrode, see Fig 5.16.

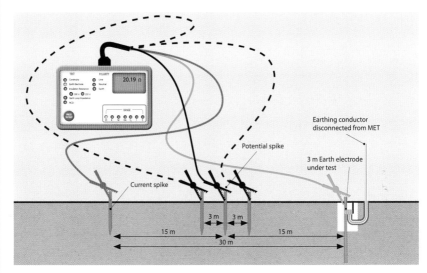

Fig 5.16 Fall-of-potential earth electrode resistance tester

There are other ways of measuring the R_a or Impedance of an Earth electrode, covered in Section 6 of this guide; however, where accuracy is paramount, the most accurate way to confirm R_a is by using a dedicated test instrument, using the fall-of-potential method.

5.8 Single-function test instruments, multi-function test instruments (MFTs) and multi-meters

Single and Multi-function Test Instruments (MFTs)

There is currently a myriad of different types of electrical installation test equipment available for the inspector to choose from. They are not, however, all the same, and some should only be used for basic tasks.

Before the electrical installation industry had a significant drive and focus on inspection and testing of electrical installations, mostly borne out of Part P of the Building Regulations in 2005, the majority of the associated test instruments came as single items of instrumentation, see Fig 5.17. This means they essentially only performed one task or two variations of the same task. They were laborious to use, bulky, and each device required individually calibrating.

Not ideal for large volume testing where individual circuit test costs became the norm in the electrical industry, so something had to evolve. Enter the one-stop-shop installation tester, the multi-function installation tester

(MFT), see Fig 5.18. This piece of equipment takes all of the individual items of test instrument and combines them into one piece of equipment, which is more portable and loans itself to high volume testing.

Either type of test equipment can be used; in some cases, especially where fault-finding is the key operation, single-function test instruments can often provide the best solution.

Fig 5.17 Single-function installation test instrument

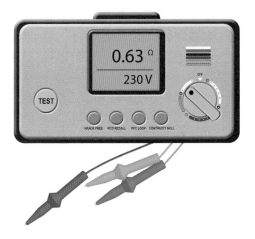

Fig 5.18 Multi-function installation test instruments (MFTs)

Multi-meters

Not to be confused with either single or multi-function installation testers, multi-meters tend to cover numerous measuring and evaluation ranges that are more suited to an electronics field, as opposed to the electrical installations industry.

Multi-meters, see Fig 5.19, are generally not calibrated, although they can be, their readings may fall outside of the requirements and manufacturing standards needed for electrical installation test equipment.

They tend to not be capable of injecting any form of voltage or measuring resistance values in a live circuit.

Multi-meters may also not be adequately rated for taking measurements on some circuits, and this must always be taken account of, before their use. Given their reduced capabilities, from an electrical installation perspective, multi-meters should only be used for basic fault finding.

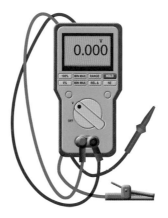

Fig 5.19 Multi-meter

5.9 Thermal evaluation equipment

Although BS 7671 does not require the use of thermal evaluation equipment, or thermal imaging techniques. These thermal surveys are becoming ever more popular ways to ascertain the condition or possible areas for concern in an Electrical Installation. Given BS 7671 highlights in multiple areas, that damage and wear from thermal effects must be taken account of, new thermal imaging technologies can be utilized, where an installation may not be accessible for a number of reasons, such as:

- Installations that cannot be shut down for commercial reasons
- Installations that may not be accessible
- Parts of an installation that require on-load evaluation
- Installation types that have historical evidence of benefiting from less invasive testing

Using thermal imaging equipment can highlight the following problems, that may not be apparent either visually or from a lack of access:

- Overloaded conductors running at higher than specified temperatures
- Lose connections that are causing overheating and thermal damage
- Unbalanced poly-phase systems with overloaded Live conductors
- Excessive Neutral conductor temperatures, which may point towards overloading or harmonic discrepancies
- EMF induced overheating caused by eddy currents in incorrectly installed equipment
- Equipment possibly receiving thermal damage from overloaded conductors

When we look at the possible uses of thermal imaging, we can see that in some cases, it makes better sense to keep the installation energized, so that we can have a better understanding of how it is actually performing in a real-world environment.

Thermal surveys can take many forms and will invariably include images of overheated areas of installation, see Fig 5.20. These images will usually be accompanied by data detailing what the actual temperatures should be, set against the findings of the surveyor, followed by an outcome of the survey to remedy any findings.

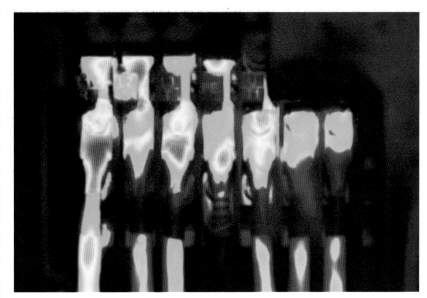

Fig 5.20 Thermal image of distribution equipment

There are many different types of thermal imaging equipment available at present, ranging from mobile phone bolt-on devices, up to dedicated devices able to produce graphical representations of findings, see Fig 5.21. We would recommend that careful choices are made to ensure the correct equipment is chosen for the surveys that are to be undertaken.

Fig 5.21 Types of thermal imaging equipment

Equally as important as the equipment chosen is the ability required to undertake this kind of work. Thermal imaging is a very specific skill set and has pitfalls of its own, given the nature of the equipment and how it sees or perceives a possible heat source. We would highly recommend anyone looking to engage in this area of contracting to take thermal imaging equipment manufacturers' advice and also undertake training prior to carrying out any form of commercial enterprise.

5.10 Calibration

Test instruments are only as accurate as the datum point that they themselves are measured against. Although there is no actual definitive frequency for calibration requirements of equipment, it is taken that a regular calibration check via a calibration service and monthly operator checks thereafter is likely to be sufficient.

When we talk about a piece of equipment's calibration certificate, we actually talking about a check against known values. Most test instruments are not designed to be calibrated or have a function for a calibration service to carry out alterations to them. If test instruments are tested and confirmed as out of calibration, when compared to the manufacturer's design parameters, it is likely that the manufacturer will need to repair them.

The reason we have a calibration carried out initially, is to confirm a known datum point that we can then use carry out in house checks on a regular basis, to confirm that the test instruments readings are still in keeping or similar to the calibration certificate's stated known values.

We can carry out in-house checks in a number of ways, depending on the equipment we are testing. Without using a proprietary checkbox, which is specifically designed for carrying out in house checks, see Fig 5.22.

Fig 5.22 Proprietary test instrument checkbox

If a checkbox is not used, a sufficient alternative will need to be found, Table 5.2 gives examples of possible alternative known sources for checking test instruments, where they are available, and any possible pitfalls there may be in using them.

Table 5.2 Alternative test instrument verification sources			
Test instrument function to be verified	Value to be verified	Possible alternative source for verification	Drawbacks and possible inaccuracies
Low ohmmeter (continuity)	Conductor resistance (Ω)	A selection of resisters, of known values that can be used to check the readings given by the test instrument, compared against the initial calibration check value	Reliant on stable connections with test leads and resistors need to be treated carefully, to ensure that their values are not altered by damage
Low ohmmeter (insulation resistance)	Insulation Resistance ($M\Omega$)	A selection of resisters, of known values that can be used to check the readings given by the test instrument, compared against the initial calibration check value	Reliant on stable connections with test leads and resistors need to be treated carefully, to ensure that their values are not altered by damage
EFLI test meter	Impedance (Ω)	A regular socket-outlet, (the same must be used each time) close to the incoming source, which can be compared against the initial calibration check value	The socket-outlet used can be damaged or worn through regular use and may give inaccurate readings over time.
RCD test meter	RCD operation time in seconds (s)	A regular RCD, (the same must be used each time) close to the incoming source, which can be compared against the initial calibration check value	If the RCD begins to deteriorate, it may be difficult to conclude if the RCD is damaged, or the test equipment is outside of its calibration

Whichever method is used, checkbox, or an alternative, it must be noted that variances in the external voltage and impedance are common. These variances in external values must also be recorded, to ensure test meter check readings are not seen as failing, when the equipment under test may be accurately indicating fluctuations in the external supply.

5.10.1 Frequency of checks

In all cases, single and multi-function test instruments must be checked regularly, and their on-going accuracy compared against a known set of readings to ensure they are still within their calibrated design parameters. Although we have mentioned earlier in this Section that monthly in-house frequencies are generally sufficient, any frequencies for accuracy checks are dependent on the level of use and amount of rough handling a piece of test equipment is subjected to. Actual frequencies and levels of checking can only be decided by the person responsible for the accuracy of any test equipment's readings in a business, based on a risk assessment; this person is usually referred to as the duty holder.

Where test equipment is either damaged, or suspected to have received damage, it must not be used again until it has been proven to be operating correctly, either by in-house accuracy checks, or full calibration. Where the casing or ancillaries of a piece of equipment has been damaged, it is strongly recommended that the manufacturer, or their licensed repairers, verify the accuracy of the damaged and repaired equipment.

5.10.2 Calibration records

Accurate records should always be kept of calibrations and in-house checks, in order to understand where equipment is within its calibrated limits, or if readings are drifting, which may indicate damage.

Although ironic it should be noted that periodically, proprietary checkboxes may need to be calibrated and compared against a known set of values, and their findings adequately recorded

Records can either be electronic or paper, providing the correct data is recorded and held for diagnostic use in the future.

Accurate records will also aid in any risk assessments which may be carried out to evaluate the on-going frequencies of checks for test instruments.

Section 6

Standard Tests

6.0 Standard Tests

6.1 Safety

During the process of any Inspection and Testing, risk to persons, livestock, equipment or property should be evaluated. Where necessary steps must be taken to ensure any danger or potential for risk is avoided. If danger or the potential for it cannot be removed, control measures must be in place to mitigate any such risk. For example, the use of barriers to prevent contact with live parts whilst covers are removed.

It is important to remember that clients are not usually electrically skilled, and therefore the process for conducting the inspection and testing should be fully communicated with them prior to starting any work. This should be documented and could form part of your duties under the 2015 CDM Regulations for certain projects.

Any verification of an installation to ensure it complies with BS 7671:2018 must be made by a skilled person, competent in that type of work. The test instruments used should be in good condition, calibrated and fit for purpose. Inspectors will need to be experienced for the type of installation being inspected and understand the inherent dangers.

6.2 Sequence of Tests

After completion of the inspection, the following tests, where relevant, should be done:

- Continuity of protective conductors
- Continuity of ring final circuit conductors
- Insulation resistance
- Polarity – dead
    – live
- Earth electrode resistance
- Earth fault loop impedance
- Additional protection and fault protection (RCD testing)
- Phase sequence (polyphase installations or circuits)
- Prospective fault current

- Functional testing (RCD and AFDD test buttons, operation of protective devices)
- Verification of voltage drop

6.3 Continuity of conductors

Regulation 643.2.1. requires the continuity of conductors and connections to exposed-conductive-parts and extraneous-conductive-parts to be verified by measurement of their resistance.

Therefore, every protective conductor, including the earthing conductor, protective bonding conductors, circuit protective conductors, and supplementary equipotential bonding conductors, will require testing. In the case of ring-final circuits, live conductors will also require testing for continuity.

The purpose of the test is to verify that the conductors are electrically sound and correctly connected using a low-resistance ohmmeter, see Section 5.2.

Preparation

Preparation of the low-resistance ohmmeter is important if realistic test readings are to be obtained:

- Check the condition of the battery using the battery check feature of the ohmmeter
- Check that test leads are securely connected

Test lead resistance nulling

With typical continuity test results being in the range of tenths of ohms, the resistance of test leads is significant and must be deducted from the final measurement, for an accurate result to be obtained.

Most test instruments have a null feature that measures the resistance of the test leads and automatically deducts this value from any readings obtained, so only the circuit conductor resistance is read.

The procedure of nulling test leads will be slightly different for each manufacturer of test equipment, but the basic principle is to connect the test leads together so the resistance can be measured and deducted from any test results, see Fig 6.1

Instruments will hold the test lead resistance in its memory for a set period, and it will not show in the test result. It is always worth checking that the setting has not changed prior to performing any tests. Simply connect your test leads together and take a continuity reading; the result should be zero if the auto-null is working.

Where an auto-null facility is not available, you will have to measure the test lead resistance and deduct it from your measurement.

It should be noted that when testing short cables with larger csa with a nulled test meter, the meter may struggle to record a value because of the very low resistance. This can be overcome by including the test lead resistance in the test and then deduct the test lead value to obtain final resistance value that should be recorded.

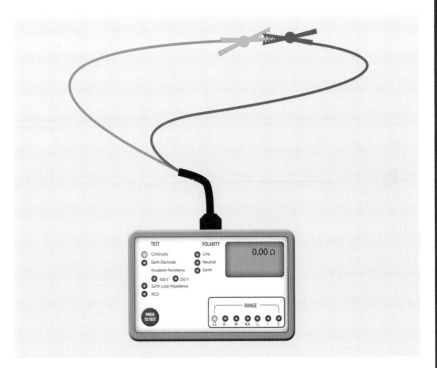

Fig 6.1 Nulling of test leads

Parallel earth return paths

Throughout this Section, reference will be made to parallel paths, and it is important to understand what is meant by this term. Simply put, a parallel earth path is an alternative route for current to flow. Sometimes this can be an advantage, for example, where you want to achieve fast disconnection of a protective device. But for testing purposes, it can be a hindrance.

Parallel earth paths are created when circuits have a common connection to a conductive part, which may be part of the electrical system or not. It may also be an intentional connection but could be accidental. In any case, care should be taken to remove any parallel earths whilst conducting certain tests to prevent false readings from being obtained.

Parallel earth paths could hide a defect within a cable or wiring system, such as no cpc continuity, and therefore, where practicable must be removed during testing. Conductive parts of an installation that often provide parallel earth return paths are:

- Installation pipework
- Metallic conduits, trunking and tray
- Metallic structural parts of the building
- Central heating and air conditioning systems
- Fly leads to metal back boxes, which are in turn fixed to the building structure

Where doubt exists about an extraneous-conductive-part

There may be doubt if an item of metalwork within an electrical installation is an extraneous-conductive-part. For example, it may be suspected that plastic pipework has been installed somewhere along the run of metal pipework. Where there is such doubt, a resistance test can be performed to test between the MET and the metal pipework in question. The value can be used in conjunction with the following formula:

$$R_x = \frac{U_0}{I_{limit}} - R_b$$

Where:

R_x the resistance between the metallic part in question and the MET

U_0 the nominal voltage line to Earth

R_b the resistance of the human body

I_{limit} the value of current through the body which must not be exceeded

The following values are given in British Standard Published Document PD 6519, IEC 60479, Guide to effects of current on human beings and livestock:

U_0 230 V

R_b 1,000 Ω (for hand-to-hand contact in dry conditions)

I_{limit} 0.01 A (the let-go threshold)

These values give the following maximum value for R_x:

$$R_x = \frac{230}{0.01} - 1000$$

$$R_x \geq 22,000 \ \Omega$$

A reading below 22,000 Ω will mean the metallic item is considered to be an extraneous-conductive-part which does require to be bonded. It is important to note that whilst carrying out this test, all cpcs associated with any items of equipment connected to the pipework being tested should be temporarily disconnected to avoid parallel paths.

Checking continuity of the Earthing conductor

Check test leads have been nulled prior to a test, See Fig 6.1.

This test may not be practical on TN-C-S systems due to limited access at the service head, so will need to be verified by inspection. The example shown in Fig 6.2 shows the Earthing conductor being tested between MET and CU.

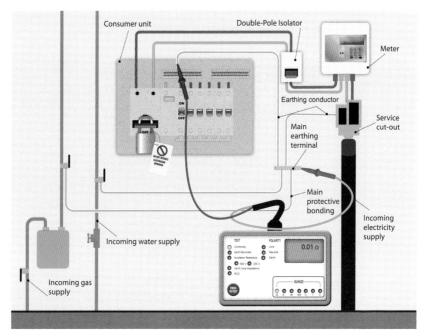

Fig 6.2 Continuity of the Earthing conductor

Checking continuity of the protective bonding conductors

Check test leads have been nulled prior to a test, See Fig 6.1.

This test is carried out by disconnecting one end of each protective bonding conductor and connecting the test leads of the low-resistance ohmmeter at either end of the protective bonding conductor. After noting the instrument reading, the ends of the protective conductors are reconnected and a final check made to confirm their effective connection, as illustrated in Fig 6.3.

It is often necessary to use a long test lead for this test, and proprietary wandering leads are available. However, a suitable length of cable can be used if care is taken to make good connections. This will involve the nulling of the combined resistance of test leads and wander lead.

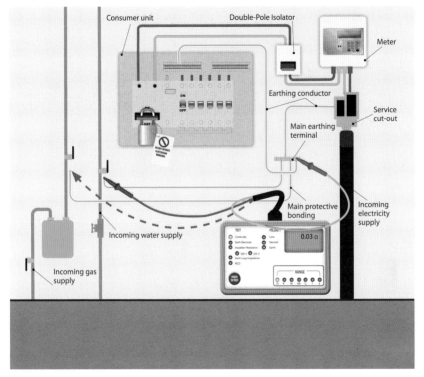

Fig 6.3 Continuity of the protective bonding

Protective bonding conductor sizes

BS 7671 is clear about the requirements for the csa of protective conductors but says nothing directly about their length. This is because the length of a protective bonding conductor isn't generally relevant.

A protective bonding conductor is designed to reduce the touch voltage of extraneous-conductive-parts in the event of a fault. By doing this, protective bonding conductors are not primarily designed to carry current and, therefore, the resistance of them is generally not an issue.

We call this linking of extraneous-conductive-parts by bonding conductors, the equipotential zone. It's equipotential because the potential difference between extraneous-conductive-parts is almost zero, therefore equal. Any potential difference between them, above zero, will allow current to flow in the event of a fault, so we try to keep any touch voltage below 50 V. It is for this reason protective bonding conductors are not length and resistance dependent.

To size the protective bonding conductors, BS 7671 gives the following requirements:

TN-S and TT

- Not less than 0.5 x csa of the Earthing Conductor
- Not less than 6 mm^2 in any scenario
- Any conductor need not be larger than 25 mm^2 copper, or its equivalent resistance if not copper

TN-C-S (PME)

- Must comply with BS 7671:2018 Table 54.8.

Conductor sizes given in the table are for copper, other conductor materials csa must have the equivalent copper resistance for their size.

Something else to remember with PME Protective bonding conductors is that they are sized in accordance with the supplier's copper equivalent csa of the PEN conductor. This can prove difficult when trying to ascertain the size and material of the neutral of the supplier's conductor. See Table 3.9 in Section 3.

That said, we are interested in the length of protective bonding conductors so that we can confirm they are the correct size and resistance.

We have to confirm by measurement, the continuity of all protective conductors to extraneous-conductive-parts in accordance with Regulation 643.2.1. We don't have to note this down on the certificate or report, but we have to ensure that the resistance reading we have is consummate with:

- The length of the conductor

And

- The csa of the conductor

By doing this, the inspector can determine if the csa of the conductor is continuous throughout its length.

Different values of copper resistance, with respect to conductor csa per/km, can be used to calculate conductor resistance, relative to its length. Table 6.1 gives these values for the most commonly used conductor csa, based on an ambient temperature of 20°C.

Table 6.1 Resistance of copper conductors by csa	
Nominal csa mm²	Maximum conductor resistance @ 20°C Ohms/km
1.5	12.1
2.5	7.41
4	4.61
6	3.08
10	1.83
16	1.15
25	0.727
35	0.524

Note

Based on the information provided by Prysmian for BS 5467 armoured cable, which publishes the DC resistance of conductors at 20°C. From this, we can calculate what the length of a conductor should be, given we know its resistivity and csa. We can see how this relates to pre-worked values in Table 6.2, which we can use to ensure that the cable we are inspecting and testing is what it appears to be.

Table 6.2 – Resistances for varying lengths of some typical copper main protective bonding conductors at 20°C										
Minimum csa (mm²)	Length in metres									
	5	10	15	20	25	30	35	40	45	50
6	0.02	0.03	0.05	0.06	0.08	0.09	0.12	0.12	0.14	0.15
10	0.01	0.02	0.03	0.04	0.05	0.05	0.06	0.07	0.08	0.09
16	0.01	0.01	0.02	0.02	0.03	0.034	0.04	0.05	0.05	0.06
25	0.004	0.007	0.01	0.02	0.02	0.02	0.03	0.03	0.03	0.04
35	0.003	0.005	0.008	0.01	0.01	0.01	0.02	0.02	0.02	0.03

Checking continuity of supplementary bonding conductors

Check test leads have been nulled prior to a test, see Fig 6.1.

This test usually requires the use of a long test lead, and therefore, the nulling of both test leads and the long lead is required.

Where additional protection is provided by supplementary bonding, there is a requirement to confirm the adequacy of connections. In some cases, the wiring will be accessible, for example, in a plant room. In such cases, the conductors, BS 951 clamps, and terminations can be verified by visual inspection.

Where BS 951 clamps are not accessible, or conductors are hidden from view, confirmation that exposed and extraneous-conductive-parts of the location have been connected together and connected to the protective conductors of all equipment in that location; can be verified by a measurement of the resistance between them.

The resistance value should be comparable to the length and csa of the conductor used; the resistance is often negligible ($<0.05\,\Omega$) with short cable runs only typically required.

In order to meet the requirements of Regulation 415.2.2 the resistance between simultaneously accessible exposed and extraneous-conductive-parts needs to meet the following condition:

- AC systems $R \leq \dfrac{50\,V}{I_a}$

- DC systems $R \leq \dfrac{120\,V}{I_a}$

Where:

I_a is the protective devices operating current in Amps

Or

I_a is the RCDs rated residual operating current $I_{\Delta n}$ in Amps

Note

For overcurrent protective devices, use the 5 s operating current

Checking cpc continuity using the long lead method

Check test leads have been nulled prior to a test.

This test usually requires the use of a long test lead, and therefore the nulling of both test leads and long lead are required, see Fig 6.1.

One end of the meter test lead is connected to the main earthing terminal in the consumer unit; the other end is used to make contact with each earthing terminal in each electrical accessory. The highest value of resistance should be recorded; this value is known as R_2. Fig 6.4 shows an individual circuit being tested.

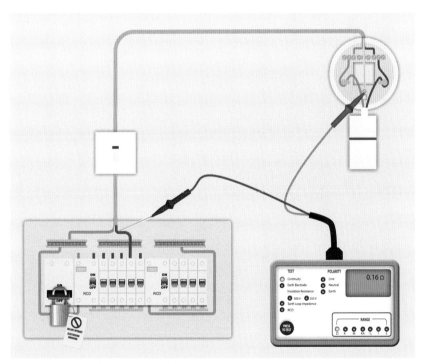

Fig 6.4 Measuring the continuity of the cpc

Checking cpc continuity and polarity

Check test leads have been nulled prior to a test, see Fig 6.1.

The previous test has, in some installations a disadvantage, in that long test leads, are required.

An alternative solution is to remove the ends of the line and circuit protective conductors from their terminals, joining them, then connecting the test leads of the low resistance ohmmeter between the line conductor and cpc terminals at every accessory. The reading taken at the most distant accessory on the circuit should be noted; this value is known as the $R_1 + R_2$ value. An example of this test is illustrated in Fig 6.5.

It is a good idea at this point to carry out a line to neutral test, as this will confirm the continuity of the neutral conductor and also confirm the correct polarity of the $R_1 + R_2$ test has been achieved. Although the L-N test is not specifically required by BS 7671, it is recommended.

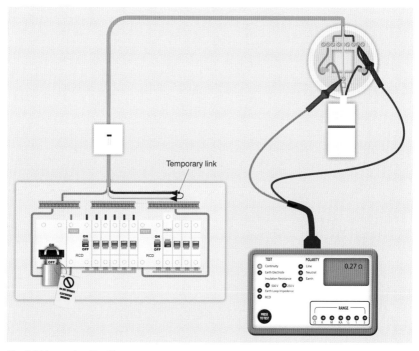

Fig 6.5 Measuring $R_1 + R_2$

Ring-final circuit continuity tests

Check test leads have been nulled prior to a test, see Fig 6.1.

This test verifies the continuity of the line, neutral, and circuit protective conductors. The test is designed to establish that the ring-final circuit is complete and is not broken.

The test is carried out using a low-resistance ohmmeter, as illustrated in Fig 6.6. The line to line, end to end value is known as r_1 the neutral to neutral, end to end test is known as r_n, and the cpc to cpc, end to end test is known as r_2.

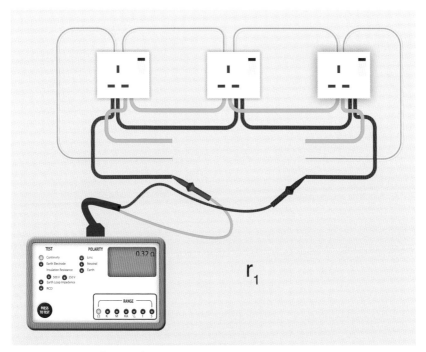

Fig 6.6 Continuity of r_1 using low-resistance ohmmeter

Step 1

Measure the end to end resistance of the line, neutral and cpc, in turn, using a low-resistance ohmmeter, as illustrated in Fig 6.6.

The value of the cpc ring will differ if the ring has a smaller csa than the line and neutral conductors. For example, a 2.5 mm² PVC T&E cable has a cpc of 1.5 mm². In this case, the resistance value of the cpc ring will be 1.67 times that of the line and neutral conductors.

This figure is derived by dividing the smaller csa into the larger, i.e., 2.5/1.5 = 1.67, and this can be carried out for any cable sizes so that the expected value can be verified.

Step 2 (figure of 8 Test)

To confirm the continuity of the ring by connecting the start of the line conductor to the return neutral conductor. Then connect the test instrument to the return of the line conductor and the start of the neutral conductor.

The resistance values obtained should be the sum of individual readings of r_1 and r_n, as shown in Fig 6.7.

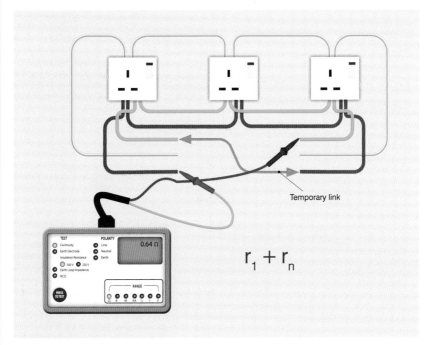

Fig 6.7 Continuity of r_1 and r_n

To confirm, there are no bridge connections in the ring circuit, connect the start of the line conductor to the return neutral conductor, the return of the line conductor, and the start of the neutral conductor. Then measure the resistance between the line and neutral at each socket-outlet, as illustrated in Fig 6.8. The resistance values obtained should be substantially the same, with readings being approximately ¼ of the $r_1 + r_n$ value.

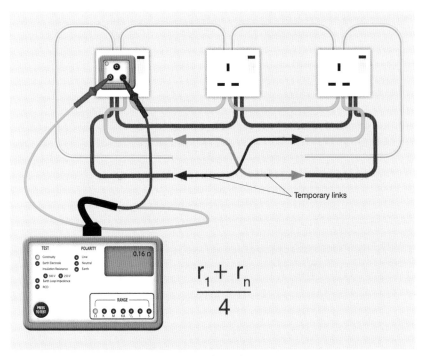

Fig 6.8 Continuity of $r_1 + r_n$ showing ¼ value formula

Step 3

Connect the start of the line conductor to the return cpc. Then connect the test instrument to the return of the line conductor and the start of the cpc. This test resistance value obtained should be the sum of individual readings of r_1 and r_2, as illustrated in Fig 6.9.

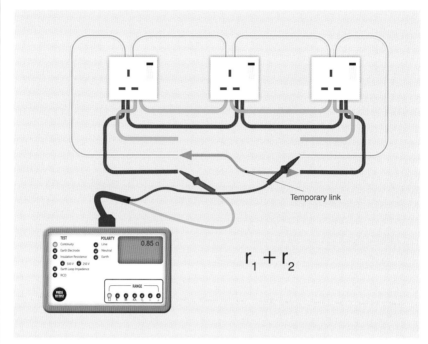

Fig 6.9 Continuity of r_1 and r_2

Now connect the start of the line conductor to the return cpc and connect the return of the line conductor and the start of the cpc. Then measure the resistance between the line and cpc at each socket-outlet, as illustrated in Fig 6.10. The resistance values obtained should be substantially the same, with readings being approximately ¼ of the $r_1 + r_2$ value. This value should be recorded on the test schedule as the $R_1 + R_2$ value for the ring-final circuit.

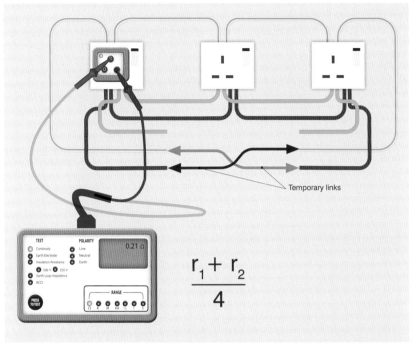

$$\frac{r_1 + r_2}{4}$$

Fig 6.10 Continuity of $r_1 + r_2$ showing ¼ value formula

Any socket-outlet wired as spurs off the ring will have higher values, which will be in proportion to the length of the spur conductor.

Verification of results
If the value of resistance at socket-outlets in Fig 6.10 is approximately a ¼ of those values in Fig 6.9, this will indicate that all socket-outlets are wired on the ring.

When the full test is correctly carried out, and the results are satisfactory, then the correct polarity will have been confirmed at each socket-outlet, as will the cpc continuity.

6.4 Insulation resistance
These sequence of tests are to verify that the insulation of circuit conductors, electrical accessories, and equipment is satisfactory, and there is no unwanted leakage between live conductors (line and neutral or line to line) and live conductors and Earth.

It is important to remember that Regulation 643.3.1 requires tests to be carried out with the circuit under test having the cpc connected to the Earthing arrangement. This will ensure any breakdown in insulation is picked up where cables are in contact with exposed-conductive-parts of the system, for example, trunking or conduit.

For single-phase circuits, the test is carried out as illustrated in Figs 6.11, 6.12 and 6.13.

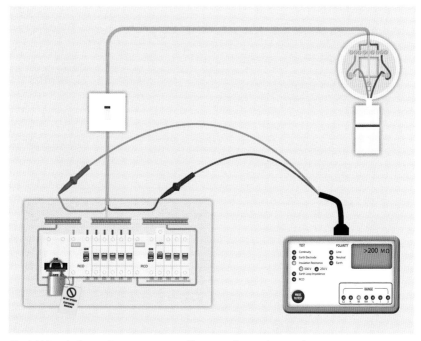

Fig 6.11 Insulation resistance measured between line and neutral

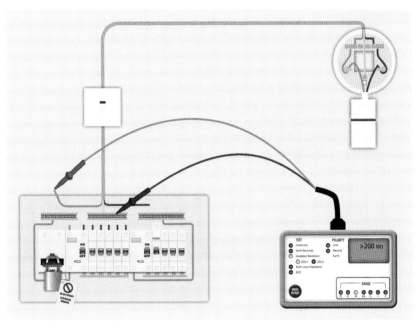

Fig 6.12 Insulation resistance measured between cpc and neutral

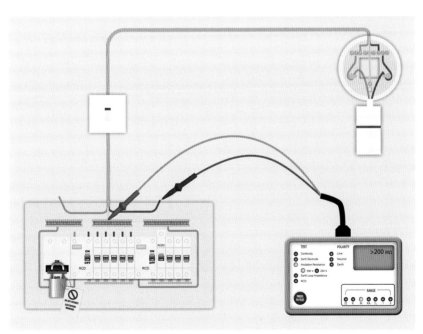

Fig 6.13 Insulation resistance measured between line and cpc

Figs 6.14, 6.15 and 6.16 show the procedure for testing the whole installation. This time the examples shown are for a three-phase installation. The distribution board's main switch is in the off position, with all circuit protective devices in the on position.

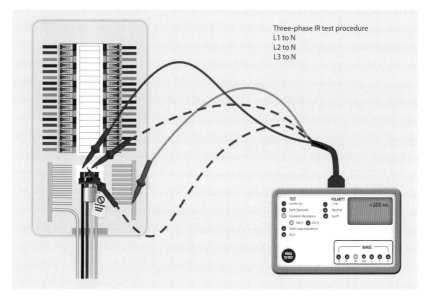

Three-phase IR test procedure
L1 to N
L2 to N
L3 to N

Fig 6.14 Insulation resistance measured between lines and neutral

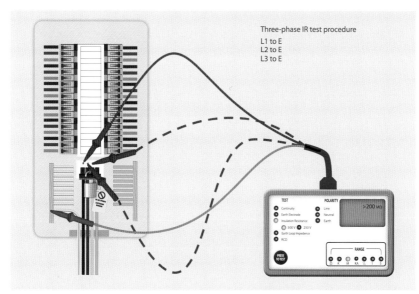

Fig 6.15 Insulation resistance measured between lines and earth

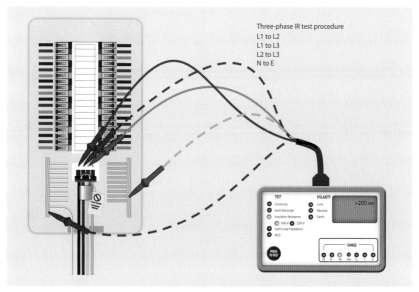

Fig 6.16 Insulation resistance measured between lines and between neutral and Earth

In order to carry out this test, an insulation resistance tester set on the MΩ range shall be used, which is capable of providing a DC test voltage in accordance with Table 64 of BS 7671. Instruments to BS EN 61557-2 will meet this requirement; see Section 5 of this Guide.

Before performing the tests, any appliances, fixed equipment, and electrical accessories vulnerable to damage from the insulation resistance test voltage should be either removed or isolated. Examples being dimmer switches, alarm panels, smoke detectors, touch switches, electronic control gear for lighting, and certain types of RCDs.

For circuits with a nominal voltage up to 500 V, the test voltage will be 500 V DC, and the minimum value of insulation resistance will be 1 MΩ. This applies to the entire installation and not individual circuits or conductors.

If a reading of less than 2 MΩ is obtained across the installation, then further investigation of the circuits is required. This would involve a breakdown of each circuit to locate the cause of the low insulation resistance.

IR general requirements

The electrical installation should be complete with all accessories in place and all switches in the 'on' position. Where lighting circuits have 2-way controls, the test will need to be carried out twice by ensuring the 2-way switches are operated on the second test to include a test of all circuit conductors, including the strappers between the 2-way switches.

Also, ensure all lamps are removed, and neon indicators in electrical accessories, capacitors, and discharge lighting fittings are disconnected to avoid poor or misleading test results. During periodic inspection and testing where it is found impractical to disconnect or remove such items, the local switch controlling the relevant item should be left in the 'off' position, and this should be an agreed limitation. If a test instrument has a kΩ range, it is good practice to perform the test using this range first, as this will highlight any connected loads or equipment.

Any equipment with exposed-conductive-parts which has been removed or isolated whilst the test was carried out, must be tested separately, as specified by the British Standard for that equipment. If a British Standard does not exist, a minimum value of insulation resistance of 1 MΩ should be used.

Insulation resistance and USB sockets

In recent years a common problem with IR testing is what to do when 13 A socket-outlets with USB charger ports are installed. Possibly the only way to get a satisfactory reading would be to disconnect all socket-outlets with USB ports, whilst maintaining the connection of the ring circuit conductors.

However, that is not practical in many cases where numerous amounts of socket-outlets have been fitted.

Socket-outlets to BS 1363-2:2016

Socket-outlets with integral USB charger ports came onto the market in 2013 as an alternative to plug-in chargers, a number of which were shown to have serious safety defects. Previously, they were not covered by a single product standard, but the introduction of BS 1363:2016 has changed that. The inclusion of these accessories in this standard brings them into line with BS 7671, which states that every socket-outlet for household and similar use should preferably be of a type complying with BS 1363 (Regulation 553.1.201).

Note

See also Regulation 559.5.1(v) concerning connections to the fixed wiring and Regulation 433.1.204 regarding ring-final circuits.

Battery-powered devices that are charged from USB charger ports normally require a supply of 5 V DC. A maximum charging capacity of up to around 3 A can be drawn from one port. Where a socket-outlet has two USB ports, both ports can be used simultaneously, with the 3.1 A charging current being split between both ports.

To convert the nominal mains voltage of 230 V AC to 5 V DC requires both reduction and rectification of the mains voltage; this is achieved efficiently using a switch-mode power supply (SMPS), which utilises a semiconductor switching technique.

The SMPS is normally connected across the line and neutral terminals and has a resistance of approximately 0.2 MΩ. Consequently, an IR test carried out between the line and neutral terminals will detect this resistance, and the reading obtained will be distorted.

Note

The electronic circuitry in an SMPS can be damaged by a 500 V DC IR test between line and neutral terminals, and the USB port may fail to function following such a test.

Insulation resistance testing options for USB combined socket-outlets

The options for IR testing of sensitive equipment such as USB socket-outlets in BS 7671 are as follows:

- Disconnect the device(s) or equipment, and test at 500 V DC
  Regulation 643.3.2 requires that any device or equipment which is likely to influence the result of an IR test, or be damaged by such a test, must be disconnected before the test is carried out.

  Disconnection may be viable where there is only a small number of socket-outlets with USB charger ports in the final circuit(s) to be tested. However, it becomes less viable as the number of these socket-outlets increases because disconnection (and reconnection) is time-consuming and introduces the possibility of the socket-outlets being wrongly reconnected. In such circumstances, the tester may well conclude that it is not reasonably practicable to disconnect the socket-outlets.

- Reduce the test voltage to 250 V DC
  Regulation 643.3.2 gives an alternative course of action where it is not reasonably practicable to disconnect vulnerable equipment, such as socket-outlets with USB charger ports. In such cases, the test voltage for the particular circuit may be reduced to 250 V DC, but the minimum insulation resistance value of Table 64, i.e., 1 MΩ, still applies.

- Do not use a test voltage of 500 V DC between live conductors
  A third option is given by Regulation 643.3.3. Where IR testing is carried out using a 500 V DC test voltage, the live conductors (i.e., line and neutral) must be connected together for the duration of the test and a measurement taken between the line/neutral connection and Earth.

This connection could be conveniently made at the consumer unit without having to disconnect the socket-outlets.

It would be acceptable to use a 500 V DC test voltage to measure between line(s) and Earth and neutral and Earth separately. However, the note to Regulation 643.3.3 advises caution and states that additional precautions, such as disconnection, may be necessary.

There is a distinct disadvantage in not testing between live conductors, as a line to neutral fault would not be detected. Such a fault could result in the operation of the protective device or, in the worst case, a fire.

IR testing can be carried out using a 250 V DC test voltage, and short-circuit faults can usually be identified by a reading, which is significantly less than the normal internal impedance of an SMPS (around 0.2 MΩ).

With the above considerations in mind, NAPIT recommends that IR tests on final circuits with socket-outlets with USB charger ports should, ideally, be carried out with a test voltage of 250 V DC for new installations and additions/alterations to an existing installation.

When carrying out a periodic inspection and testing on final circuits containing socket-outlets with USB charger ports, a limitation on IR testing of such circuits could be considered.

Insulation resistance and Surge Protective Devices (SPDs)

In those installations with SPDs present within the fixed wiring, the IR test will activate those SPDs and give a false reading. The test will not damage the SPD, irrespective of the test impulse applied to the SPD, as the energy is a very low level:

- 1000 V will activate SPDs
- 500 V may activate SPDs
- 250 V is a safe level to avoid activating the SPD

Firstly, it is a requirement that the presence of SPDs are labelled in section 534.4.1.7, so if the label is missing this should be corrected.

Methods of SPD isolation can be operating the OCPD (MCCB, CB or fuse carrier) in the SPDA or surge protective device assembly or removing the plugs of pluggable SPDs; failing these options, the disconnection or removal of the PE conductor on the SPD.

Remember to turn back on, or reconnect, after testing. Some type 3 SPDs could be in extra deep socket boxes or within trunking. So be aware of this should you get error readings during tests.

Insulation resistance and AFDDs

AFDDs are very complex devices that are monitored internally by a microprocessor-controlled system. These controllers are electronically sensitive and use an internal power supply, fed by the incoming supply to the device. Being electronically sensitive AFDDs are susceptible to voltage surges, and carry some, minimal, surge protection internally. When we carry out insulation resistance (IR) tests to circuits protected by AFDD, great care needs to be taken, as IR test voltages in excess of 250 V are very likely to damage and render the devices inoperative, see Fig 6.17.

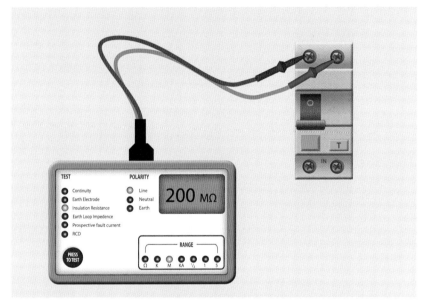

Fig 6.17 Direct IR testing. Not recommended for AFDD, unless reduced test voltage is applied.

Remember that when these devices detect that they are no longer capable of operating, they shut down and will not allow the circuit to re-energize, so if an excessive IR voltage is applied, the device will most likely need to be replaced.

Insulation resistance for circuits incorporating SELV

In order to verify the requirements of BS 7671 Section 414 (discussed in Section 3), the separation of live parts from other circuits and from Earth needs to be verified by measurement of the insulation resistance.

The test voltage applied should be in accordance with BS 7671 Table 64, which is 250 V DC. The minimum acceptable insulation resistance value is 0.5 MΩ.

Insulation resistance for circuits incorporating PELV

In order to verify the requirements of BS 7671 Section 414 (discussed in Section 3), the separation of live parts from other circuits needs to be verified by measurement of the insulation resistance.

The test voltage applied should be in accordance with BS 7671 Table 64, which is 250 V DC. The minimum acceptable insulation resistance value is 0.5 MΩ.

6.5 Polarity

Dead installation

This test is carried out using a low resistance ohmmeter to verify that all single-pole circuit-breakers and fuses are in the line conductors only. It is also used to ensure that Edison Screw lamp holders with centre contacts to BS EN 60238 are connected to the line conductor, and the outer screwed contact to the neutral. This is not necessary when the lamp holders are of the E14 or E27 type.

When continuity of circuit protective conductors has been verified using the R_1+R_2 test method, then confirmation of correct polarity on some circuits may have been achieved as well.

It is a requirement of Regulation 643.6 (iii) to check wiring has been correctly connected throughout the installation.

Live installation

The polarity of the supply at the origin should be verified before the installation is energised. This can be achieved using a voltage indicating device or approved test lamp with leads complying with GS 38. Live polarity testing throughout the installation can be achieved when carrying out the earth fault loop impedance tests illustrated in Fig 6.18.

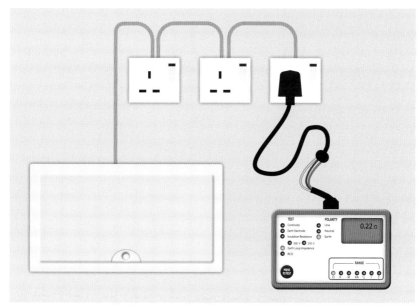

Fig 6.18 Earth fault loop impedance test, also used to verify polarity

6.6 Earth electrode resistance test

This test is carried out to ensure that a low resistance path to Earth is provided, for example, when fault protection is provided by the use of an RCD on a TT system.

Safety

Care must be taken with Earth resistance testing, and risks must be assessed by the person undertaking the test. It is recommended that rubber protective gloves and rubber safety mats are used for certain applications such as testing for substation grounding due to the possibility of a fault in the power system causing current to flow into the Earthing system.

There are three basic methods for measuring the resistance of installation earth electrodes:

1. Fall-of-potential method (three-terminal test)
2. Dead Earth method (two-point test)
3. Clamp-on test method (stakeless)

For all of these tests only the resistance of the electrode is measured. This method is used where a high level of accuracy is important and where low values of electrode resistance to earth are required, as in electrodes used in the earthing of sub-stations, generators and transformers. These methods involve the use of a proprietary test instrument.

Measurement using a dedicated soil resistivity/earth electrode tester
This method of testing is usually used where an electricity supply is not available. Dedicated earth electrode resistance testers are available from different manufacturers. The test leads to the test probes, and earth electrode under test must be in accordance with the manufacturer's instructions.

The earth electrode test requires the use of two temporary probes and is carried out as follows:

- Isolate the electrical installation if connected to the supply at the main switch, verify the electrical supply is off using an approved voltage indicating device, lock off and label
- Disconnect the earthing conductor from the earth electrode
- Prepare the test instrument for use, check that the instrument, test leads and test probes are in good condition and suitable for use
- Insert the temporary test probes into the ground with the test. Distances given are based on an electrode length of 3 m and the distances should be 10 x the length of any electrode, as illustrated in Fig 6.19.

Connection to the earth electrode is made using terminals C1 and P1 of a four-terminal test meter. To be able to exclude the resistance of the test leads from the reading, individual leads should be taken from the test instrument terminals and connected separately to the earth electrode under test and the temporary test probes, as illustrated in Fig 6.19.

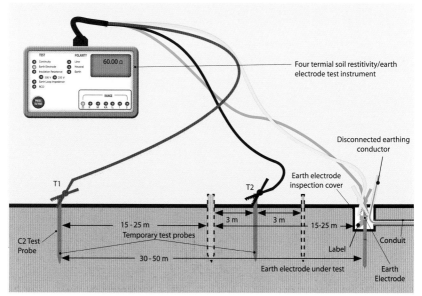

Fig 6.19 Fall of potential method of Earth electrode resistance measurement

Where the resistance of the test leads is negligible the test meter C1 and P1 terminals may be linked together and a single test lead used, as would be the case if using a three terminal test meter.

Take the following three resistance readings:

- With the potential test probe T2 inserted in the soil midway between the electrode under test and the current test probe T1
- With the potential test probe, T2 moved to position three metres back towards the electrode under test
- With the potential test probe, T2 moved to a position three metres from its original position towards test probes T1

The distance between the test probes is very important. If they are too close together, their resistance areas will overlap, resulting in an inaccurate value of resistance for the earth electrode under test.

In order to obtain reliable results, the distance between the electrode under test and the current test probe C2 should be at least ten times the maximum dimensions of the electrode system. As an example, when the earth electrode under test is three metres long, a distance of thirty metres is required.

On completion of the test and a satisfactory resistance reading, reconnect the earthing conductor to the earth electrode, remove the main switch locking device and label and restore the electrical supply.

Measurement using an earth fault loop impedance test instrument
Alternatively, the measurement can be achieved using an earth fault loop impedance tester, in which the impedance of the whole earth fault current path is measured and is taken to be the resistance of the electrode. This method is used where a high level of accuracy is not strictly required.

The earth electrode test is illustrated in Fig 6.20 and carried out as follows:

- Isolate the electrical installation at the main switch, verify the electrical supply is off using a voltage indicating device with proving unit, lock off and label

- Disconnect the earthing conductor to the earth electrode at the main earthing terminal (this method allows the test current to flow through the earth electrode alone and reduces the likelihood of any problems with parallel earth paths)

- Prepare the test meter for use, check that the test meter, leads, probes, and clips are suitable for use

- Connect one lead of the earth loop impedance test instrument to the earthing conductor going to the earth electrode, then connect the other lead to the line conductor at the incoming side of the main switch for the installation and carry out the test

- Record the reading which should be taken to be the earth electrode resistance

- Reconnect the earthing conductor, remove the main switch locking device and label, restore the electricity supply.

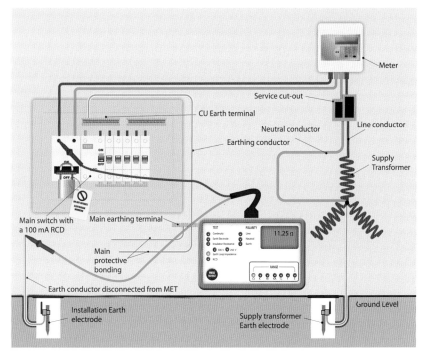

Fig 6.20 Measurement of Earth electrode resistance in a TT system using earth fault loop impedance tester

6.7 Earth fault loop impedance

External loop impedance (Z_e)

An earth fault loop impedance value may be measured using a an earth fault loop impedance tester. The main switch on the consumer unit should be turned off and made secure to isolate the installation from the source of supply. The Earthing conductor on TN-S and TN-C-S supply systems is disconnected from the main earthing terminal and the earth fault loop impedance tester connected between the incoming supply line conductor and the end of the earthing conductor, as illustrated in Fig 6.21.

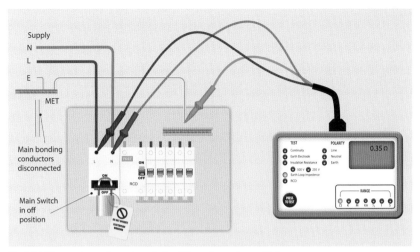

Fig 6.21 Measuring external earth fault loop impedance (Z_e)

Fig 6.21 shows that the main bonding conductors have been disconnected to ensure that the supplier's Earthing arrangement is tested and not affected by any parallel paths. Care must be taken to ensure that they are reconnected after the test and before the installation is energised.

An alternative method of obtaining a value of Z_e is to make enquires from the electrical supplier. Typical values are:

- TN-S system 0.8 Ω
- TN-C-S system 0.35 Ω

Note
The measured value must be obtained to ensure compliance with earth fault loop impedance testing Z_s values.

Earth fault loop impedance (Z_s)
This test is carried out to ensure that the required disconnection times for each circuit in an installation will be achieved if a fault to Earth occurs.

Differing from the Z_e test, the Z_s test is the measurement of both the external and internal earth fault loop impedance combined. The internal impedance is essentially the $R_1 + R_2$ value of the circuit combined with the Z_e of the installation, which can be denoted by the following formula:

$$Z_s = Z_e + (R_1 + R_2)$$

Using an earth fault loop impedance tester, the loop impedance of each circuit is measured at the final point, as illustrated in the lighting circuit in Fig 6.22.

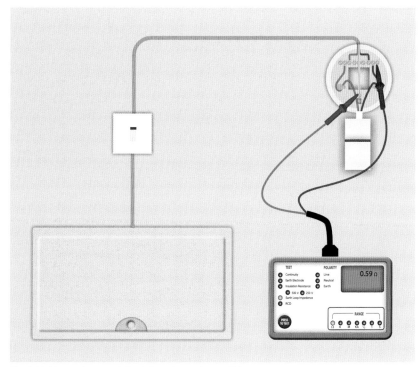

Fig 6.22 Measuring earth fault loop impedance (Z_s)

The measured values should be compared with maximum permitted values, given in Tables 41.2. to 41.4 of BS 7671, when corrected by multiplying the appropriate value by 0.8, as detailed in Appendix 3 of BS 7671. 80% Z_s values are given for various commonly used devices in Table 6.3.

Table 6.3 80% device Z$_s$ values

Overcurrent protective device (OCPD) Rating AMPS	BS 88-2 E bolt & G clip		BS 88-3 Fuse Sys. C		BS 3036 Fuse		BS 1361/2 Fuse BS 1362 (Plug Top)		BS 3871 TYPE 1	BS 3871 TYPE 2	BS 3871 TYPE 3	BS EN 60898 / BS EN 61009-1 B	BS EN 60898 / BS EN 61009-1 C*	BS EN 60898 / BS EN 61009-1 D*
	0.4 s	5 s	0.4 s	5 s	0.4 s	5 s	0.4 s	5 s	0.4/5 s	0.4/5 s	0.4/5 s	0.4/5 s	0.4/5 s	0.4 s
2	26.5	35.2	N/A	N/A	N/A	N/A	N/A	N/A	N/A	N/A	N/A	N/A	N/A	N/A
3	N/A	N/A	N/A	N/A	N/A	N/A	12.48	17.60	N/A	N/A	N/A	11.66	N/A	N/A
4	12.5	16.8	N/A	N/A	N/A	N/A	N/A	N/A	N/A	N/A	N/A	N/A	N/A	N/A
5	N/A	N/A	7.94	11.68	7.28	13.44	7.94	12.44	8.74	4.99	3.50	N/A	N/A	N/A
6	6.24	9.60	N/A	N/A	N/A	N/A	N/A	N/A	7.22	4.08	2.91	5.82	2.91	1.45
10	3.72	5.44	N/A	N/A	N/A	N/A	N/A	N/A	4.37	2.50	1.75	3.49	1.75	0.87
13	N/A	N/A	N/A	N/A	N/A	N/A	1.83	2.90	N/A	N/A	N/A	N/A	N/A	N/A
15	N/A	N/A	N/A	N/A	1.94	4.06	2.48	3.8	2.85	1.66	1.16	N/A	N/A	N/A
16	1.94	3.20	1.84	3.12	N/A	N/A	N/A	N/A	2.66	1.56	1.09	2.18	1.09	0.54
20	1.34	2.24	1.54	2.56	1.34	2.91	1.29	2.13	2.18	1.25	0.87	1.75	0.87	0.44
25	1.03	1.76	N/A	N/A	N/A	N/A	N/A	N/A	1.75	1.00	0.70	1.39	0.69	0.35
30	N/A	N/A	N/A	N/A	0.83	2.00	0.87	1.39	1.46	0.83	0.58	N/A	N/A	N/A
32	0.79	1.36	0.73	1.28	N/A	N/A	N/A	N/A	1.37	0.78	0.55	1.10	0.55	0.27
40	0.60	1.04	N/A	N/A	N/A	N/A	N/A	N/A	1.09	0.62	0.44	0.87	0.44	0.22
45	N/A	N/A	0.46	0.80	0.45	1.20	N/A	0.72	0.97	0.55	0.39	0.77	0.38	0.19
50	0.46	0.79	N/A	N/A	N/A	N/A	N/A	N/A	0.87	0.50	0.35	0.69	0.35	0.17
60	N/A	N/A	N/A	N/A	0.32	0.86	N/A	0.53	N/A	N/A	N/A	N/A	N/A	N/A
63	0.35	0.62	0.29	0.54	N/A	N/A	N/A	N/A	0.69	0.40	0.28	0.55	0.28	0.13
80	N/A	0.44	N/A	0.41	N/A	N/A	N/A	0.38	0.55	0.31	0.22	0.43	0.22	0.10
100	N/A	0.34	N/A	0.30	N/A	0.40	N/A	0.26	0.44	0.25	0.17	0.34	0.17	0.07
125	N/A	0.26	N/A	N/A	N/A	N/A	N/A	N/A	N/A	N/A	N/A	0.27	0.13	0.06
160	N/A	0.21	N/A	N/A	N/A	N/A	N/A	N/A	N/A	N/A	N/A	N/A	N/A	N/A
200	N/A	0.14	N/A	N/A	N/A	N/A	N/A	N/A	N/A	N/A	N/A	N/A	N/A	N/A
250	N/A	N/A	N/A	N/A	N/A	N/A	N/A	N/A	N/A	N/A	N/A	N/A	N/A	N/A

*For BS EN 60898 / 61009 Type 'D' 5 Sec. Please use Type 'C' Column.

The value of measured Z_s for each circuit can be compared to the calculated Z_s, which is obtained by adding the R_1+R_2 value of resistance for each circuit to the value of Z_e.

$$Z_s = Z_e + (R_1 + R_2)$$

Discrepancies between Z_s and $Z_e + (R_1 + R_2)$

Whilst, in theory, the measured Z_s value should match the sum of $Z_s = Z_e + (R_1+R_2)$. In reality, it often doesn't. Inspectors will need to understand possible reasons for any discrepancies to be able to confidently record the test result as accurate.

The following list provides some examples of common discrepancies:

- For cable designs that have been compiled using a declared value of Z_e. Comparison of the results (during initial verification) between the circuit design Z_s and the actual measured Z_s value could be considerably different if the actual Z_e is different from the value used for the design

- An allowance will need to be made for the actual ambient temperature present during testing

- The installer may have chosen a different route for the cable, resulting in a different conductor length. This could account for discrepancies between design and measured Z_s values

- The installer may have used a different sized cable to the csa specified in the design, perhaps using a bigger cable because that's all that was on the van.

- Circuits with RCDs in place are generally tested using the low current 'no-trip' range on the meter, allowing a Z_s value to be taken without tripping the RCD. Higher than expected Z_s readings are often produced due to the characteristics of this testing arrangement

- Where accessories are connected to something that introduces parallel paths, for example, metallic conduit or tray work, the extra parallel earth return paths will provide a lower earth fault loop impedance result than expected.

Manufacturers Data

Designers will often use manufacturer's data, specific to the actual protective devices specified for the installation when designing circuits. Maximum values of earth fault loop impedance can vary between manufacturer's and therefore, BS 7671 uses more onerous values than some may quote.

Inspectors need to be aware of this in case they have a situation where Z_s readings don't comply with the Regulations but may conform to manufacturer's data, which may provide a more favourable outcome.

6.8 Prospective fault current I_{pf}

Where it is required to verify the prospective fault current at the origin of an installation and any other relevant positions, this can be achieved by measurement/calculation or by inquiry with the DNO.

The measurement of prospective fault current is carried out using an earth fault loop impedance tester connected across the line conductor and Earth at the origin of the installation. This gives the value of Z_s.

Using Ohm's law, the prospective fault current can be calculated:

$$I_{pf} = \frac{U_0}{Z_s}$$

I_{pf} Prospective fault current
U_0 Nominal voltage to Earth
Z_s Earth fault loop impedance

Many earth fault loop impedance testers, and MFTs have a prospective fault current I_{pf} range, giving readings in kA.

When measuring I_{pf} all, Earthing and Bonding must be in place to ensure the highest prospective fault characteristics are obtained.

For three-phase distribution boards and circuits, the measurement can be taken between each line and earth, with the highest value being recorded.

Measuring prospective fault current

When completing a test certificate for an installation, the prospective short-circuit current value is usually used. The prospective fault current I_{pf} measured in kA is the higher value of prospective short-circuit current P_{scc} and prospective earth fault circuit current P_{efc}.

The difference being P_{scc}, illustrated in Fig 6.23, is measured between line and neutral conductors at the origin of the installation, and P_{efc} is measured between line and earth conductor at the origin of the installations, illustrated in Fig 6.24.

For three-phase distribution boards and circuits, measurement can be taken between each line and neutral, with the highest value being noted. If the test instrument is capable of a direct line to line measurement, then this should also be completed to obtain the worst-case prospective short-circuit current. The highest prospective fault current occurs when there is a simultaneous fault between all line conductors.

BS 7671 Appendix 14 provides guidance on the determination of prospective fault current and advises that where measurement between line conductors is not possible, inspectors shall take the Line to Neutral fault current and multiple by 2.

Section 434 of BS 7671 only considers the case of a fault between conductors belonging to the same circuit. Therefore, for a single-phase circuit, the higher of the line to neutral or line to earth prospective fault current is applicable, and for a three-phase circuit the three-line fault prospective fault current is applicable.

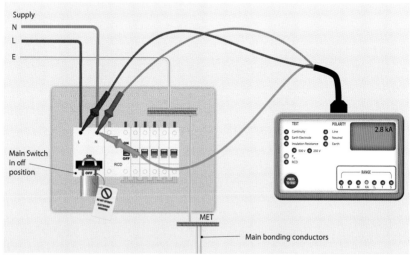

Fig 6.23 Measuring Line to Neutral prospective short-circuit current

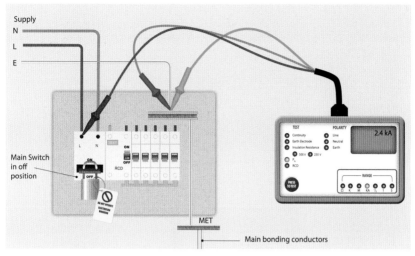

Fig 6.24 Measuring prospective earth fault current

6.9 Testing RCDs

Ever since we started to install RCDs for additional protection, the method for testing their functionality hasn't changed a great deal. RCD evolution, however, has moved on from a mostly electromechanical nature to ever more sensitive electronic devices, with some devices requiring a functional earth connection, to establish an earth reference point to allow them to operate correctly.

The historic $1 \times I_{\Delta n}$ and $5 \times I_{\Delta n}$, testing criteria for RCDs not exceeding 30 mA, each required a defined operating time maximum (see Table 6.4), to prove that the device was safe for continued use. The upper operating limit could also be used to gauge the life cycle of a device, to see if it was becoming less effective by approaching the upper limit as consequent periodic inspections took place, even if the maximum values are never reached.

Table 6.4		
RCD Type	$1 \times I_{\Delta n}$ (ms)	$5 \times I_{\Delta n}$ (ms)
BS 4293	200	40
BS 7288 SRCD (socket-outlet)	200	40
BS EN 61008	300	40
BS EN 61009	300	40

Additional protection

With the introduction of BS 7671:2018 18th Edition of the IET Wiring Regulations, the requirement for the 1 x $I_{\Delta n}$ test has diminished for all RCDs being used for additional protection, i.e., those up to and including 30 mA.

Regulation 415.1.1 gives the requirements for additional protection by ≤ 30 mA RCDs and Regulation 643.8 provides guidance on testing. When an RCD with a rated residual operating current $I_{\Delta n}$, not exceeding 30 mA is used to provide additional protection, a suitable RCD tester should be used to verify the device will open within 40 ms with a test current of 5 $I_{\Delta n}$ (150 mA) or higher. Instruments conforming to BS EN 61557-6 will meet this requirement.

Although the basis for testing the functionality of an RCD have altered within BS 7671:2018, testing devices not exceeding 30 mA at 1 x $I_{\Delta n}$ and 5 x $I_{\Delta n}$, as Table 6.4 depicts, is still good practice and can give ongoing indications of the life cycle of RCDs, and ultimately their ability to protect life.

When testing RCDs, their first trip at 1x $I_{\Delta n}$ could be the first instance the device has tripped in a considerable time, if it is not being periodically tested via the test push button. Should the next 1x $I_{\Delta n}$ test be significantly quicker, this would give an indication to the tester that the device is not being tested and advice can be given on the report accordingly.

Industry guidance for testing RCDs has always been to ensure that equipment is not connected to them and that the RCD is effectively alone in its circuit. This protocol is no longer strictly accurate, and other factors now need to be taken account of.

There are significantly different types of RCDs now available, and they are designed for differing equipment types. It is vital that as an Inspector you know what their differences are and how they should be used. Table 3.6 in Section 3 lays out the different RCD types and examples of equipment types that they are designed to operate with.

The tests should be carried out with an RCD tester set at 0° then, repeated when set at 180° with the longest operating time being noted. Fig 6.25 shows the procedure for testing RCDs, where test leads are connected to the load side of the RCD.

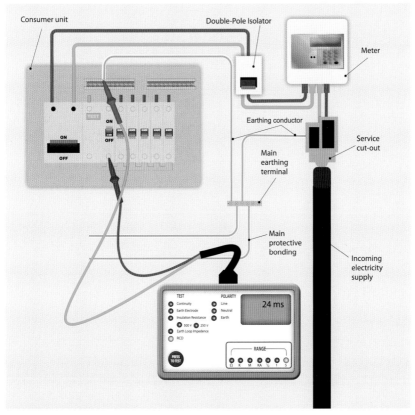

Fig 6.25 Two lead RCD test

The RCD test button should be operated to ensure the device operates; this should be done after the previous test and not before, see functional testing Section 6.9 of this Guide. This is to give a true representation of the device's ability to operate, without being manually operated to free up the moving parts, prior to any testing.

6.10 Phase sequence and phase rotation (polyphase installations or circuits)

For polyphase circuits, Regulation 643.9 requires phase sequence to be maintained throughout the installation. Phase sequence is confirmed by continuity testing and the checking of polarity throughout the installation, with phase rotation confirmed using a phase rotation meter, see Section 5.6 of this Guide.

Phase rotation tests should be carried out at each part of the installation by connecting the test leads of the phase rotation meter to the terminals of the equipment under test, as follows:

- L1 test lead to terminal L1
- L2 test lead to terminal L2
- L3 test lead to terminal L3

The rotation should be noted; this may be indicated by direction (clockwise or anti-clockwise), or by indicating lamps (L1-L2-L3). Correct rotation is usually considered to be clockwise or L1-L2-L3.

Whilst phase rotation is important for rotating equipment, phase sequence throughout the installation should not be overlooked. For example, a three-phase socket-outlet circuit should have the L1 conductor connected to L1 of the protective device and L1 terminals of each socket-outlet and so on for the other conductors. Should the phases cross between outlets and then cross back, the rotation will be ok at the start of the circuit and end of the circuit, but unless checked at all socket-outlets, a hidden danger could go undetected. See Fig 6.26. Imagine an industrial machinery workshop has a change around, and a rotating machine that has always spun in the correct direction now gets plugged into the outlet with incorrect phase rotation.

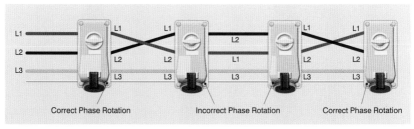

Fig 6.26 Socket-outlet circuit with incorrect phase sequence

A convenient way of ensuring phase sequence is maintained is by continuity measurement. The correct phase sequence can be confirmed using a low ohmmeter instrument to confirm that each line conductor and neutral conductor of a circuit is correctly located at their respective terminals. Either the $R_1 + R_2$ method or long lead method can be used. For the $R_1 + R_2$ method, connect L1 to CPC at the origin of the circuit and take a measurement between L1 and CPC at each point. Repeat the test for each line to confirm phase sequence has been maintained throughout, see Fig 6.27.

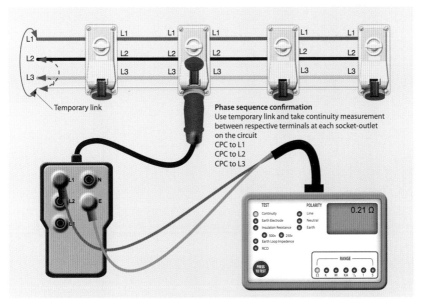

Fig 6.27 Phase sequence verified by continuity test

6.11 Functional tests

Regulation 643.10 covers the requirements of functional testing. RCDs should be operated six-monthly using the test button, which operates the integral test device. This device enables the electrical and mechanical parts of an RCD to be verified by pressing the button marked 'T' or 'Test'. There is also a requirement to operate the test button of an AFDD (where fitted) on initial verification.

All switchgear, controls, and accessory switches should be functionally tested by operating them to confirm they work and are correctly installed.

6.12 Arc Fault Detection Devices (AFDD)

As AFDDs have now been introduced as a recommendation, by BS 7671:2018 Regulation 421.1.7, Inspectors and Testers will need to understand how to check the operation of these devices and what to watch out for when carrying out testing procedures.

First off, some AFDDs have a functional test button, which can be periodically operated, to ensure the device cycles and operates as it should. The test button checks the manual disconnection systems of the device, in much the same way as the functional test button of an RCD. There is no set frequency of test button operation, unlike RCDs, which should be functionally tested, via the test button, every 6 months. When carrying out an EICR, the Client should be consulted before the test button operation of AFDDs; remember that operational limitations, as well as inspection and test limitations, may restrict some devices and circuits from full inspection and test. After this is confirmed and agreed, the functional test is a basic test; once pressed, the AFDD should disconnect, and the tell-tale window may show an amber flag, see Fig 6.28, dependent on manufacturers' specifications, to denote it has been tested.

If the AFDD tell-tale window is showing a colour, other than its normal operating state colour, it is denoting either that:

1. It has detected a fault and disconnected the circuit, or
2. It has carried out a self-test on its internal systems, which have failed.

In either case, the device will disconnect the circuit to ensure safety. If the device has detected a fault and disconnected, it will only remake the circuit if the fault has been removed; if the fault re-occurs, the device will activate again.

In normal operation, without any faults, the tell-tale window will show a healthy state, in some manufacturers' equipment, this is a green flag see Fig 6.28.

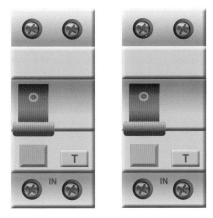

Fig 6.28 AFDD tell-tale options

6.13 Verification of voltage drop

Verification of voltage drop is not normally required during initial verification; this has been assumed to have been carried out at the design stage.

Voltage drop values are given in Appendix 4 of BS 7671. For low voltage installations fed from a public distribution system, use the values from Table 6.5

Where the distribution of the electrical system is not a public supply, e.g., a generator or transformer, etc. owned by the Client, and therefore control of the voltage bands is the responsibility of the Client, values of voltage drop can be increased as can be seen in Table 6.6.

Table 6.5 Values of voltage drop for a public distribution system	
LIGHTING	OTHER
3%	5%

Table 6.6 Values of voltage drop for a privately-owned distribution system	
LIGHTING	OTHER
6%	8%

Where design details are not available, and there is a need to verify voltage drop, for example, where a circuit has been extended, or equipment has been replaced with different load characteristics. There are two ways of verifying voltage drop:

- Calculation method
- Conductor measurement method

Calculation method

In order to be able to calculate volt drop, the conductor csa and type will be needed. The Tables in Appendix 4 of BS 7671 have a voltage drop section in which the millivolt per amp per metre (mV/A/m) of a particular cable may be obtained; for example, Table 4D5 should be used for thermoplastic insulated and sheathed flat cables with copper conductors.

The design current (I_b) will also be needed, which is fairly straight forward to obtain where there is a set connected load. But for some circuits, there is no control over what equipment is used, e.g., socket-outlet circuits; in such cases, the rating of the protective device should be used.

Lastly, the circuit length will need to be measured/estimated. The voltage drop is calculated from:

$$\text{Volt drop} = \frac{\text{(mV/A/m) x design current }(I_b)\text{ x length of run in metres (L)}}{1000}$$

For a lighting circuit at 3% of the nominal 230 V single-phase supply voltage, the voltage drop must not exceed 6.9 V. Other circuits at 5% must not exceed 11.5 V.

Three-phase power circuits at 400 V must not exceed 20 V.

Conductor measurement method

To obtain a basic indication of volt drop by measurement, a voltage measurement can be taken directly at the equipment's terminals (if safe to do so), whilst the equipment is under load. The result can be compared to the voltage present at the origin; although it will be difficult to take simultaneous readings, it should provide an indication.

For single-phase circuits, a measurement between live conductors (Line and Neutral) can be taken with an earth fault loop impedance meter. The result will need to be adjusted for the conductor's maximum operating temperature. Assuming an ambient temperature of 20°C, use a multiplier of 1.2 for a conductor operating temperature of 70°C.

To obtain the volt drop value, multiply the corrected conductor Line - Neutral loop impedance value by the design current (I_b).

VD= (Line - Neutral loop value) x 1.2 x I_b

6.14 Test readings documentation

All readings obtained from tests, or where these have not been carried out for some other reasons, must be accurately recorded on to the 'Schedule of test results'. The model form provided in BS 7671 Appendix 6 page 483, can be used for this purpose, but as this is a model, the inspector or their company are permitted to develop their own versions, provided they contain no less relevant information. The Schedule of test results is the same for both the EIC and the EICR. The MEIWC, does not require a full schedule of test results, as the the form itself contains the required data fields to be populated.

An example of a 'Schedule of test results', can be seen in Figure 6.29.

NAPIT *Electrical Installation Test Sheet*
Requirements for Electrical Installations – BS 7671:2018 (IET Wiring Regulations 18th Edition)

NA/EICR

Page 5 of

© Copyright NAPIT January 2018

Complete in every case

Client

Installation address

Postcode

Location of distribution board

Distribution board designation

Number of ways

Complete only if the distribution board is not connected directly to the origin of the installation

Supply to DB is from

Overcurrent protective device for the distribution circuit:

Type BS(EN)

Supply polarity confirmed

No. of phases

Rating

Phase sequence confirmed

Nominal Voltage

V

A

Characteristics at this distribution board

Zdb

Ipf

Ω

kA

Associated RCD (if any): BS (EN)

No. of poles

Above 30mA

Operating at

$^1 I_{\Delta n}$

ms

30mA or below

Operating at

$I_{\Delta n}$

mA

$5 I_{\Delta n}$

Time Delay (if applicable)

ms

Test instrument serial number(s)

Loop imped.

Insulation resistance

Continuity

RCD

CIRCUIT DETAILS

Circuit designation

Circuit No. and line No.

Type of wiring

Ref. method

No. of points served

Circuit conductor csa — L/N (mm²)

Circuit conductor csa — CPC (mm²)

Maximum disconnection time (BS 7671) (s)

Overcurrent protective devices

BS EN Number

Type No.

Rating (A)

Breaking Capacity (kA)

RCD operating current $I_{\Delta n}$ (mA)

BS 7671 Max permitted value Zs / Other Ω

TEST RESULTS

Circuit impedance Ω

Ring final circuits only (measured end to end) — r_1, r_n, r_2

All circuits to be completed using $R_1 + R_n$ or R_2, not both — Fig 8 check ($\checkmark$), R_1+R_n, R_2

Insulation resistance (Record lower reading)

Test Voltage V

L/L L/N (MΩ)

L/E N/E (MΩ)

Polarity

Max. measured Z_s (Ω)

RCD testing

Above 30mA $I_{\Delta n}$ ms

30mA below $5 I_{\Delta n}$ ms

Manual test button operation

RCD ($\checkmark$)

AFDD ($\checkmark$)

Details of Circuits and/or installed equipment vulnerable to damage when testing

Date(s) dead testing

To

Date(s) live testing

To

See attached sheets page(s)

Of

Tested by: Name (capital letters)

Position

Signature

Date

Wiring Types: A PVC/PVC B PVC cables in metallic conduit C PVC cables in non-metallic conduit D PVC cables in metallic trunking E PVC cables in non-metallic trunking F PVC/SWA cables G SWA/XPLE cables H Mineral insulated O Other

NAPIT 4th Floor, Mill 3, Pleasley Vale Business Park, Mansfield, Nottinghamshire NG19 8RL

NA/EICR/D001 (V1)

Fig 6.29 Schedule of test results

The following breakdown is based on the NAPIT test schedule shown in Fig 6.29.

- Column ❶ contains the circuit number. Each circuit is identified with a number; usually, the consumer unit is marked starting from the main switch (but not always).

- Column ❷ contains a circuit description; due to limited space, this can only be used as a general indicator; extra detail may need to be provided on an extra schedule.

- Column ❸ requires the Inspector to note the type of wiring used, a study of the test schedule will reveal a key for different wiring types. For example, standard domestic cable PVC twin and earth (PVC T&E) is shown as wiring type A.

- Column ❹ requires the Inspector to provide the installation Reference Method. There are numerous methods for installing cables, known as Reference Methods, and these have an alphabetical or numerical reference. Commonly used Reference Methods and the maximum rating for PVC T&E cable can be seen in Table 6.7.

- Column ❺ requires the Inspector to insert the number of points on the circuit, e.g. the number of lights, the number of sockets, etc.

- The next two columns ❻ & ❼ concern the size of conductors; as part of the inspection, the Inspector will be confirming cable sizes are appropriate for load and installation conditions and the size is noted here.

- Column ❽ contains the maximum disconnection time as required by BS 7671. Most final circuits will either be 0.4 seconds or 0.2 seconds, depending on the system type. Distribution circuits are permitted to have a disconnection time not exceeding 1 or 5 seconds.

- The next four columns ❾ to ⓬ concern details of the overcurrent protective device installed and require the following:

  - The BS EN number of the circuit's protective device to be listed.

  - The protective device Type to be also listed. Different fuses and circuit-breakers have different characteristics, allowing them to be selected for a particular purpose.

  - The rating of the device to be listed, e.g. 6 Amp (common size for lighting circuits), etc.

  - The breaking capacity of the protective device to be listed – The Inspector needs to confirm that under fault conditions, the device can handle the amount of current that it will be subjected to.

- Column ⓭ requires the Inspector to record RCD operating current (where fitted), for most domestic arrangements this will be 30 mA.

- Column **14** requires the Inspector to record the maximum earth fault loop impedance for the corresponding protective device. In simple terms, the longer the circuit, the more the resistance will be increased, and the less current will flow. When there is a fault, there needs to be sufficient fault current flowing to operate the protective device (blow the fuse).

- Columns **15** to **18** are used to record continuity values for final ring circuits; basically, the Inspector is checking all conductors are wired correctly and are continuous with no breaks in continuity.

- Columns **19** and **20** are used to record either the sum of resistances of the line conductor added to the earth conductor (circuit protective conductor (CPC)), this test is known as the $R_1 + R_2$ test; or alternatively, the resistance of just the CPC can be recorded; this is known as the R_2 value.

- Columns **21** to **23** concern insulation resistance. This test is carried out to verify that the insulation of circuit conductors, electrical accessories and equipment is satisfactory and there is no unwanted leakage between live conductors (line and neutral) and between live conductors and earth. The Inspector will also need to state what test voltage is applied, 500 V DC is the maximum test voltage; however, this is often dropped to 250 V DC when conducting EICRs, due to the possibility of damaging equipment that may still be connected.

- Column **24** requires the Inspector to confirm correct polarity, basically checking that the wiring has been correctly connected throughout the installation. This can be carried out by inspection and/or testing.

- Column **25** is for recording the results of the earth fault loop impedance test. This test is carried out at the final point of the circuit, and the result is compared with the maximum permitted earth fault loop impedance, which is listed in column **14**.

- Column **26** and **27** is used by the Inspector to record the results of the RCD tests. Different RCDs have different parameters; for example, 30 mA RCDs are required to operate within 40 ms when subjected to a test current 150 mA or higher.

  - The last two columns **28** and **29** require a tick from the Inspector to confirm that the functional testing of any RCDs or Arc Fault Detection Devices (AFDDs)

Table 6.7 Installation Reference Methods and Conductor csa Current Ratings for PVC Insulated Flat Cable with Protective Conductor (PVC T&E)

Ref. description	Installation Ref. method	Conductor cross-sectional area						
		1.0 mm²	1.5 mm²	2.5 mm²	4.0 mm²	6.0 mm²	10.0 mm²	16.0 mm²
A	Enclosed in conduit in an insulated wall	11.5 A	14.5 A	20 A	26 A	32 A	44 A	57 A
B	Enclosed in conduit or trunking on a wall, etc.	13 A	16.5 A	23 A	30 A	38 A	52 A	69 A
C	Clipped direct	16 A	20 A	27 A	37 A	47 A	64 A	85 A
100	In contact with a plasterboard ceiling or joists covered by thermal insulation not exceeding 100 mm	13 A	16 A	21 A	27 A	34 A	45 A	57 A
101	In contact with the plasterboard ceiling or joists covered by thermal insulation exceeding 100 mm	10.5 A	13 A	17 A	22 A	27 A	36 A	46 A
102	In a stud wall, with thermal insulation, with cable touching the wall	13 A	16 A	21 A	27 A	35 A	47 A	63 A
103	Surrounded by thermal insulation, including within a stud wall, with thermal insulation, with cable not touching the wall	8 A	10 A	13.5 A	17.5 A	23.5 A	32 A	42.5 A

Completed Documentation

Once a Schedule of test results is complete, it must be attached and numbered accordingly, to the rest of any documentation for either an EIC or EICR. There may be more than one Schedule of test results, as it is common to produce one for each DB/CU, or area of an installation, to aid understanding and maintenance in the future.

This page has been intentionally left blank

Section 7

Initial Verification

7.0 Initial Verification

7.1 Verification Process

In order to comply with the requirements of BS 7671:2018, steps must be taken to ensure that during installation and before any circuits are energised and put into service, that any work done conforms to BS 7671:2018. Therefore, inspection, testing, and certification are carried out to ensure compliance with the relevant requirements of BS 7671.

The inspection shall be based on the application of the design for the electrical installation to ensure that those aspects of the design have been correctly selected, installed, and verified for correct operation. For installations where the person carrying out the inspection and testing is also the person who carried out the design to multiple persons carrying out design, construction, inspection and testing. The Electrical Installation Certificate (EIC) model forms recognise all types of scenarios.

Responsibilities of Signatories
The EIC clearly sets out what responsibilities are being signed for, with design, construction, and inspection and testing separated. It would be unreasonable to hold inspectors responsible for a part of the installation that they had no control over, i.e., design and construction. Therefore, to allow verification of the installation to be conducted correctly, the Inspector will require comprehensive information to be provided.

Minimum information required
Prior to the commencement of any inspection, Regulation 641.2 requires the following information shall be made available to the person carrying out the inspection and testing:

Assessment of general characteristics, including:

- Maximum demand (after considering diversity) for a new installation or addition
- Nominal voltage, load currents, and frequency of supply
- Prospective fault current (I_{pf}) at the origin of the installation
- Value of external earth fault loop impedance Z_e
- Type and rating of the protective device(s) at the origin of the circuit
- Diagrams and charts providing information on:

- The type of circuits
- Number of points
- Number and size of conductors
- The type of wiring systems
- Location and type of protective devices
- Location of isolation and switching devices

Details of characteristics of:

- Protective devices for automatic disconnection
- Earthing arrangements
- Circuit impedances
- Description of methods used to comply with BS 7671
- Inspectors will need to be made aware of any equipment that may be vulnerable to testing; the following devices are either sensitive or may give spurious readings under certain tests:
- Dimmer switches
- Fire Detection and Fire Alarm Systems
- Data and Computer equipment
- Intruder alarms
- SPDs
- Home automation or smart home controls
- Automation controls
- AFDDs

Inspection

Initial verification inspections must precede any testing and should take place with that part of the installation disconnected from the supply as required by Regulation 642.1.

In some installations, the inspection may be an ongoing process through to the completion of the installation works. In these cases, adequate inspection and test sheets should be kept throughout to aid the final inspection and testing including any documentation requirements.

An inspection shall include verification that any installed electrical equipment:

- Is to a British, European, International Standard or its equivalent
- Is correctly selected and erected
- Is not visibly damaged or defective so as to impair safety

Items relevant to an installation that should be inspected are listed in Regulation 642.3, with further items listed in BS 7671 Appendix 6. Example inspection items are as follows:

- Connection of conductors
- Identification of conductors
- Routing of cables in safe zones/protection against mechanical damage
- Selection of conductors for current-carrying capacity and voltage drop
- Connection of single-pole devices for protection or switching in line conductors only
- Correct connection of accessories and equipment
- Presence of fire barriers and protection against thermal effects
- Methods of protection against electric shock
- Prevention of mutual detrimental influences
- Adequate provision of isolating and switching devices and their location
- Undervoltage protective devices
- Correct labelling of protective devices, switches, and terminals
- Adequate access to electrical equipment, including switchgear and any connections or joints
- Correct selection and installation of SPDs where required
- Adequate measures to protect against the effects of electromagnetic disturbances
- Alternative supplies and their arrangements

Any special requirements called for in Part 7 of BS 7671 that are relevant to installation should also be inspected.

EIC Schedule of Inspections

BS 7671 provides a checklist for larger installations and a model form that can be used for new installation work for domestic and similar premises with a supply up to 100 A. It should be noted that it is acceptable to modify the standard schedule to suit specific installations, providing all items that require verification are listed in order to confirm compliance with the relevant clauses in BS 7671.

The outcomes of each inspection item can be marked either with a tick or N/A on the schedule of inspections. Because EICs are used for new work, the work must either be fully compliant or N/A to the installation.

7.2 Description of Initial Verification items

1.0 External Condition Of Intake Equipment (Visual Inspection Only) Where inadequacies are encountered, it is recommended that the person ordering the report informs the appropriate authority

1.1	Service cable
1.2	Service head
1.3	Earthing arrangement
1.4	Meter tails
1.5	Metering equipment
1.6	Isolator (where present)

2.0 Parallel Or Switched Alternative Sources Of Supply

2.1	Adequate arrangements where a generating set operates as a switched alternative to the public supply (551.6)
2.2	Adequate arrangements where a generating set operates in parallel with the public supply (551.7)

Fig 7.1 Extract of EIC inspection schedule sections 1 and 2

Inspection Items 1.0 to 1.6: External condition of intake equipment (visual inspection only) Fig 7.1

This section of the inspection schedule is dedicated to the condition of the intake equipment. The equipment in this area of the installation is owned by the DNO and the meter operator; therefore, the Inspector does not have permission to undertake an intrusive inspection. Comments and outcomes can only be based on the results of visual inspection of the external condition.

A visual inspection will include looking for any mechanical damage or signs of thermal damage to the equipment. Meter tails and protective earthing conductor sizes should be verified to ensure they are sufficient for the installation's maximum demand and earthing requirements. The health of cable insulation can be verified to ensure there is no mechanical damage and no signs of overloading, thermal damage, cracks, or splits to the insulation.

The adequacy of any cabling support can also be verified to ensure there is no strain on the conductors or associated terminals.

Inspection items 2.0 to 2.2: Parallel or switched alternative sources of supply, see Fig 7.1
These inspection items concern installations where generating sets are operating either:

- Operating as an alternative to the public supply (such as a standby generator), or
- In parallel to the public supply (such as solar PV)

Where installations contain alternative sources of supply, Inspectors will need to confirm the requirements listed in Chapter 55 of BS 7671 are met. Where the generator set is used as a switched alternative to the public supply, suitable precautions are required to prevent the generator from running in parallel to the public supply. Inspectors should check that the relevant parts of Chapter 46 and Section 537 regarding isolation have been complied with. See Regulation 551.6 for further guidance.

Where the generator set operates in parallel to the public supply, Inspectors will need to ensure the following conditions are met:

- Protection against thermal effects (Chapter 42) and protection against overcurrent (Chapter 43) shall remain effective in all situations
- Where additional protection is provided by ≤30 mA RCD for the generator circuit, the RCD must disconnect all live conductors, including the neutral conductor. See Regulation 551.7.1 for further guidance.

3.0 Automatic Disconnection Of Supply, Presence And Adequacy Of Earthing And Protective Bonding Arrangements	
3.1	Distributor's earthing arrangement (542.1.2.1; 542.1.2.2)
3.2	Installation earth electrode (where applicable) (542.1.2.3)
3.3	Earthing conductor and connections, including accessibility (542.3; 543.3.2)
3.4	Main protective bonding conductors and connections, including accessibility (411.3.1.2; 543.3.2; Section 544.1)
3.5	Provision of safety electrical earthing/bonding labels at all appropriate locations (514.13)
3.6	RCD(s) provided for fault protection (411.4.204; 411.5.3)

Fig 7.2 Extract of EIC inspection schedule sections 3

Inspection Items 3.0 to 3.6: Automatic disconnection of supply, see Fig 7.2
Inspectors will need to confirm the presence and adequacy of the earthing and protective bonding arrangements within the installation. The following items will require inspection:

Distributors earthing arrangement:

- For TN-S systems, confirmation is required that there is an adequate connection between the supplier's earth (which is usually the cable sheath) and the installations MET, as required by Regulation 542.1.2.1

- For TN-C-S systems, confirmation is required that there is an adequate connection between the neutral of the source of supply and the installations MET, as required by Regulation 542.1.2.2. This connection will need to be made by the distributor.

Installation earth electrode (where applicable):

- For TT or IT systems, confirmation is required that there is an adequate connection between the earth electrode and the installations MET, as required by Regulation 542.1.2.3.

Earthing conductor and connections, including accessibility:

- Confirmation is needed that the correct size of earthing conductor has been installed, with electrically and mechanically sound connections that are labelled in accordance with the requirements of Regulation 514.13.1(i). Connections and joints should be accessible as required by Regulation 543.3.2.

If the earthing conductor has been sized using the adiabatic equation in accordance with Regulation 543.1.3, this information should be available for the Inspector. Alternatively, the csa may have been selected in accordance with Regulation 543.1.4; see Table 7.1.

Where the earthing conductor has been buried in the ground, the minimum csa should be in accordance with BS 7671 Table 54.1; a representation of this can be seen in Table 7.2.

Table 7.1 Minimum cross-sectional area of protective conductor in relation to the cross-sectional area of associated line conductor

Cross-sectional area of line conductor S	Minimum cross-sectional area of the protective conductor (with reference to the line conductor)	
	Where protective conductor and line conductor material are the same	Where protective conductor and line conductor material are different
(mm²)	(mm²)	(mm²)
Where S is less than or equal to 16	S	$\dfrac{k_1}{k_2} \times S$
Where S is greater than 16 but less than or equal to 35	16	$\dfrac{k_1}{k_2} \times 16$
Where S is greater than 35	$\dfrac{S}{2}$	$\dfrac{k_1}{k_2} \times \dfrac{S}{2}$

Where k_1 is the value of k for the line conductor, selected from Table 43.1 in Chapter 43 of BS 7671 according to the materials of both conductor and insulation. k_2 is the value of k for the protective conductor, selected from Tables 54.2, 54.3, 54.4, 54.5 and 54.6 of BS 7671 as applicable.

Table 7.2 Minimum csa of a buried earthing conductor

Earthing conductor	Earthing conductor protected against mechanical damage	Earthing conductor not protected against mechanical damage
Protection against corrosion (sheathed conductor)	2.5 mm² copper 10 mm² steel	16 mm² copper 16 mm² coated steel
No protection against corrosion (bare conductor)	25 mm² copper 50 mm² steel	25 mm² copper 50 mm² steel

Main protective bonding conductors and connections, including accessibility:

- Confirmation is needed that the correct size of the protective bonding conductor has been installed, with electrically and mechanically sound connections that are labelled in accordance with the requirements of Regulation 514.13.1(ii). Connections and joints should be accessible as required by Regulation 543.3.2.

All extraneous-conductive-parts within the installation should be connected to the installations MET, as required by Regulation 411.3.1.2, and therefore, verification is required for all bonded parts. For TN-S and TT supplies, the conductor csa shall not be less than half the csa required for the Earthing conductor of the installation and must not be less than 6 mm², see Table 7.3.

The minimum csa for main protective bonding conductors for PME supplies shall be selected in accordance with BS 7671 Table 54.8, summarised below in Table 7.4.

Note

PME protective bonding is sized in relation to the PEN conductor and can result in larger conductors being required.

Table 7.3 Protective bonding sizes for TN-S and TT supplies

TN-S and TT supplies		
csa of Line conductor mm^2	csa of Earthing conductor mm^2	csa of Protective bonding conductor mm^2
16	16	10
25	16	10
35	16	10
50	25	16
70	35	25*

*The csa need not exceed 25 mm^2 if copper or equivalent conductance

Table 7.4 TN-C-S (PME) Protective bonding conductor sizes

Copper equivalent csa of the PEN conductor mm^2	csa of Protective bonding conductor mm^2
35 or less	10
over 35 up to 50	16
over 50 up to 95	25
over 95 up to 150	35
over 150	50

Provision of safety electrical earthing/bonding labels at all appropriate locations:

- Regulation 514.13.1 requires durable labels to be permanently fixed in a prominent position at:

    1. Earthing conductor connection points, including connections to earth electrodes, and

    2. Bonding conductor connection points to extraneous-conductive-parts, and

    3. The MET, where separate from the main switchgear

The label should read 'Safety Electrical Connection- Do Not Remove', see Fig 7.3

BS 951 Earthing clamp

Fig 7.3 BS 951 Earth clamp tag

4.0 Basic Protection, Presence And Adequacy Of Measures To Provide Basic Protection (Prevention Of Contact With Live Parts) Within The Installation

4.1	Insulation of live parts e.g. conductors completely covered with durable insulating material (416.1)
4.2	Barriers or enclosures e.g. correct IP rating (416.2)

5.0 Additional Protection, Presence And Effectiveness Of Additional Protection Methods

5.1	RCD(s) not exceeding 30 mA operating current (415.1; Part 7), see Item 8.14 of this schedule
5.2	Supplementary bonding (415.2; Part 7)

6.0 Other Methods Of Protection, Presence And Effectiveness Of Methods Which Give Both Basic And Fault Protection

6.1	SELV system, including the source and associated circuits (Section 414)
6.2	PELV system, including the source and associated circuits (Section 414)
6.3	Double or reinforced insulation i.e. Class II or equivalent equipment and associated circuits (Section 412)
6.4	Electrical separation for one item of equipment e.g. shaver supply unit (Section 413)

Fig 7.4 Extract of EIC inspection schedule sections 4, 5 and 6

Inspection items 4.0 to 4.2: Basic protection, see Fig 7.4

Inspectors will need to confirm the presence and adequacy of measures to prevent contact with live parts within the installation (basic protection). The following items will require inspection:

Insulation of live parts:

- For example, conductors being fully covered by durable insulation that can only be removed by destruction as required by Regulation 416.1. For equipment, insulation providing basic protection will need to meet the product standard of that equipment.

Barriers or enclosures:

- Where barriers or enclosures are used to prevent contact with live parts, the minimum degree of protection should be IPXXB or IP2X. IP2X equates to a hole size of 12.5 mm in diameter, which is deemed suitable to prevent contact with live parts with a finger. Regulation 416.2.1 advises of situations where larger openings are necessary for the proper functioning of equipment or to replace parts, suitable precautions shall be taken.

For any readily accessible barriers or enclosures, the horizontal top surface must have a minimum degree of protection of at least IPXXD or IP4X. IP4X equates to a hole size of 1 mm in diameter, which is deemed suitable to prevent contact with live parts with a wire.

Inspection items 5.0 to 5.2: Additional protection, see Fig 7.4
Inspectors will need to confirm the presence and effectiveness of additional protection methods:

- Where RCDs with a current rating not exceeding 30 mA are used for additional protection in accordance with Regulation 415.1. Inspectors will need to ensure the device is of the correct rating and functioning correctly in order to be effective in the event of failure of basic protection and/or fault protection. Various Regulations require the use of 30 mA RCDs for life protection and to protect against the carelessness of users. These are listed in inspection item 8.14 of this section.

- Where supplementary bonding is used for additional protection, Inspectors will need to confirm that the correct size of conductor has been installed, with electrically and mechanically sound connections that are labelled in accordance with the requirements of Regulation 514.13.1(ii). confirmation is required that all simultaneously accessible exposed-conductive-parts of fixed equipment and extraneous-conductive-parts are connected together and connected to the protective conductors of equipment in that location.

Inspection items 6.0 to 6.4: Other methods of protection, see Fig 7.4

Inspectors will need to confirm the presence and effectiveness of methods which give both basic and fault protection:

SELV and PELV systems:

- Where a SELV or PELV system has been used as a protective measure, Inspectors will need to confirm that the requirements of Section 414 have been met. Regulation 414.3 provides a list of suitable sources that may be used for SELV and PELV systems, such as a safety isolating transformer. Inspectors will need to confirm that the source is suitable, e.g., safety isolating transformer to BS EN 61558-2-6 or BS EN 61558-2-8.

  Socket-outlets and luminaire supporting couplers used in SELV/PELV systems require the use of a plug, which is different (dimensionally) to any other system used in the same installation. SELV plugs and socket-outlets shall not have a protective conductor contact.

Double or reinforced insulation:

- Where double or reinforced insulation is used, i.e., Class II or equivalent, Inspectors will need to confirm that the requirements of Section 412 have been met. Where used, basic protection is provided by basic insulation, and fault protection is provided by the supplementary insulation, or basic and fault protection is provided by reinforced insulation aimed at preventing a dangerous voltage on accessible parts of equipment if a fault occurs in the basic insulation.

  Where a whole installation relies on this protective measure, or a circuit relies purely on the use of equipment with double or reinforced equipment. Great care is needed to ensure that no changes can be made to impair the effectiveness of the protective measure. Inspectors will need to verify that there are suitable precautions in place, such as acceptable supervision. Regulation 412.1.2 prevents the use of socket-outlets with an earthing contact and luminaire supporting couplers (LSC), cable couplers, and devices for connecting luminaire (DCL). It also states that where the user may change items of equipment without authorization, this protective measure shall not be used.

Electrical separation:

- Where electrical separation is used as a protective measure, Inspectors will need to confirm that the requirements of Section 413 have been met. Confirmation is needed that basic protection is in place to prevent contact with live parts, and fault protection is provided by simple separation. Simple separation is usually provided by the use of an isolating transformer; therefore, Inspectors will need to confirm the correct type has been installed. For example, Section 722 permits one electric vehicle to be supplied from one unearthed source using a fixed isolating transformer complying with BS EN 61558-2-4.

Electrical separation is usually limited to the supply of one item of current-using equipment, where more than one item of equipment is supplied from an unearthed source with simple separation; inspectors will need to ensure the requirements of Regulation 418.3 have been met.

7.0 Consumer Unit(s) / Distribution Board(s)

7.1	Adequacy of access and working space for items of electrical equipment including switchgear (132.12)
7.2	Components are suitable according to assembly manufacturer's instructions or literature (536.4.203)
7.3	Presence of linked main switch(es) (462.1.201)
7.4	Isolators, for every circuit or group of circuits and all items of equipment (462.2)
7.5	Suitability of enclosure(s) for IP and fire ratings (416.2; 421.1.6; 421.1.201; 526.5)
7.6	Protection against mechanical damage where cables enter equipment (522.8.1; 522.8.5; 522.8.11)
7.7	Confirmation that ALL conductor connections are correctly located in terminals and are tight and secure (526.1)
7.8	Avoidance of heating effects where cables enter ferromagnetic enclosures e.g. steel (521.5)
7.9	Selection of correct type and ratings of circuit protective devices for overcurrent and fault protection (411.3.2; 411.4, 411.5, 411.6; Sections 432, 433, 537.3.1.1)
7.10	**Presence of appropriate circuit charts, warning and other notices:**
7.10.1	Provision of circuit charts/schedules or equivalent forms of information (514.9)
7.10.2	Warning notice of method of isolation where live parts not capable of being isolated by a single device (514.11)
7.10.3	Periodic inspection and testing notice (514.12.1)
7.10.4	RCD six-monthly test notice; where required (514.12.2)
7.10.5	AFDD six-monthly test notice; where required
7.10.6	Warning notice of non-standard (mixed) colours of conductors' present (514.14)
7.11	Presence of labels to indicate the purpose of switchgear and protective devices (514.1.1; 514.8)

Fig 7.5 Extract of EIC inspection schedule sections 7 and 7.10

Inspection items 7.0 to 7.11: Consumer units and distribution boards, see Fig 7.5

- **7.1** Concerns the adequacy of working space and access to consumer units, distribution boards, and switchgear. Regulation 132.12 requires sufficient space for the initial installation but also for future replacements. All equipment must be accessible for operation, maintenance, inspection and testing, and repair.

- **7.2** Requires verification that components are suitable according to assembly manufacturers' instructions or literature. For new installations or consumer unit/distribution unit replacements, usually, the same manufacturer of equipment is selected. Therefore, meeting the requirements of Regulation 536.4.203 regarding the compatibility of components for the final enclosed arrangement. Where different manufacturers' components have been used, verification is required for the suitability of the final enclosed arrangement by the original manufacturer of the assembly.

- **7.3** Requires confirmation that each electrical installation has a main linked switch or linked circuit breaker at the origin for switching and isolation purposes. All standard consumer units and distribution boards have these fitted as standard. For single-phase supplies to consumer units that will be operated by ordinary persons, the main switch must interrupt both live conductors as required by Regulation 462.1.201.

- **7.4** Requires confirmation that every circuit is provided with a means of isolation. In most cases, it is acceptable to deem the circuit-breaker as adequate to meet this requirement or the main switch to isolate a group of circuits. See Section 3 regarding the requirements for switching neutrals.

- **7.5** Concerns the suitability of the enclosure(s) for IP and fire ratings. For IP requirements, see inspection item 4 (barriers or enclosures). With regards to fire ratings, the materials used for the enclosure will have to comply with the resistance of heat and fire requirements of a suitable product standard. The materials need to withstand the highest temperature produced by the electrical equipment that will be present during normal conditions. For domestic installations, Regulation 421.1.201 requires non-combustible enclosures for consumer units and similar switchgear. Alternatively, the consumer unit or switchgear can be enclosed in a non-combustible cabinet or enclosure, providing access is not restricted.

- **7.6** Requires verification that adequate protection is in place to prevent mechanical damage to cable sheaths and insulation, where cables enter equipment. The wiring system shall be constructed with no sharp edges on any cable supports or enclosures, therefore preventing damage during installation, use, or maintenance.

- **7.7** Requires confirmation that all conductor connections are correctly located in their respective terminals and are tight and secure in order to provide durable electrical continuity and suitable mechanical strength. For successful terminations, it is essential that the manufacturer's instructions are taken into account regarding the type and number of conductors suited to each terminal. Verification of torque settings may need to be witnessed by the Inspector or confirmation by the constructor of the electrical installation that it has been done correctly. Usually, visual indication marks are painted on the terminal as part of the torque tightening process. Where cables are disturbed for testing purposes, they will need to be re-terminated and torqued appropriately using manufacturers' literature. See example consumer unit and bolt torque settings in Tables 7.5 and 7.6.

Table 7.5 Example consumer unit torque settings

Torque Settings	Pz No.	(mm)	(mm)	Cables > 1.5 mm² Tightening Torque (Nm) Single Cable	Multi Cables	Cables< 1.5 mm² Tightening Torque (Nm) Single Cable	Multi Cable	Cable Stripping (mm)
Consumer unit terminals								
Earth and neutral terminal bars	2	6.5	-	-	2	2	1.5	1.5	10
Isolation								
SB switch disconnectors	2	6.5	-	-	3.6	3.6	3.6	3.6	15
Circuit protection								
MTN CB	2	6.5	-	-	2.8	2.8	2.8	2.8	13
MBN/NCN/NDN CB	2	6.5	-	-	2.8	2.8	2.8	2.8	13
RCBO	2	5.5	-	-	2.1	2.1	2.1	2.1	13
RCCB	2	5.5	-	-	2.8	2.8	2.8	2.8	13

Table 7.6 Example bolt torque settings

TORQUE SETTINGS	
BOLTS (GRADE 8.8)	
Fixing Size	**Torque**
M5	6 Nm
M6	10 Nm
M8	24 Nm
M10	47 Nm
M12	83 Nm

- **7.8** To avoid the build-up of circulating currents (known as eddy currents) and the effects of heat in ferromagnetic enclosures. Verification is required that all line conductors, neutral conductors, and associated protective conductors enter through the same hole. Where this is not achievable, they may enter through individual holes with slots cut between them (providing the integrity of the IP rating is not compromised).

- **7.9** Requires confirmation that all protective devices are the correct type and rating with regards to overcurrent and fault protection. Inspectors will need to ensure that disconnection times can be met in order to achieve ADS; therefore, this will also require confirmation that the earthing arrangements are suitable for the particular type of system. Where protective devices are providing protection against both overload and fault current (which is the usual arrangement in most cases), the device must be capable of breaking any overcurrent up to the maximum prospective fault current (I_{pf}) at the point where the device is installed. Additionally, circuit-breakers must also be able to make the circuit under these conditions. Regulation 434.5.1 requires the rated short-circuit breaking capacity of each protective device shall not be less than the maximum I_{pf} at the point where the device is installed. There is an exception to this, where devices with a lower-rated breaking capacity are backed up by a device installed on the supply side that has the necessary rated short-circuit breaking capacity. In such cases, it may be necessary to check manufacturers' technical data to ensure the energy let-through level does not exceed the level which can be withstood without damage by the lower-rated device on the load side. For functional switching and control purposes, the device shall be in accordance with BS 7671 Table 537.4, which provides guidance on the selection of protective devices, isolation, and switching.

- **7.10** Requires confirmation that all relevant circuits charts, warning, and other notices are in place:

Provision of circuit charts/schedules or equivalent forms of information:

- Confirmation is required that a legible diagram, chart, or table, or equivalent form of information is provided within or adjacent to the CU or DB. Indicating in particular:

  - The type and composition of each circuit
  - Points of utilisation served
  - Number and size of conductors
  - Type of wiring
  - The method used for compliance with Regulation 410.3.2, which requires that protective measures shall consist of an appropriate combination of a provision for basic protection and independent provision for fault protection. Alternatively, an enhanced protective measure may be used, which provides both basic and fault protection, such as reinforced insulation.

- Information needed for the identification of devices providing protection, isolation, and switching
- Circuits or equipment vulnerable to electrical testing

For simple installations, the information may be given in a schedule; see Table 7.7 for a CU circuit chart example.

Type of circuit	Points served	Live conductor mm²	Circuit protective conductor mm²	Protective device	Type of wiring
Table 7.7 Consumer unit circuit chart					
Smoke alarm	Fire alarm system	1	1	6 A Type B	PVC/PVC
RCD 1 (30 mA)					
Spare					
Downstairs lights	6 lights	1	1	6 A Type B	PVC/PVC
Upstairs sockets	10 sockets	2.5	1.5	32 A Type B	PVC/PVC
Cooker	1 kitchen	6	2.5	32 A Type B	PVC/PVC
RCD 2 (30 mA)					
Upstairs lights	7 lights	1	1	6 A Type B	PVC/PVC
Bathrooms lights	3 lights	1	1	6 A Type B	PVC/PVC
Downstairs sockets	10 sockets	2.5	1.5	32 A Type B	PVC/PVC
Kitchen sockets	8 sockets	2.5	1.5	32 A Type B	PVC/PVC
Shower	1 shower	10	4	40 A Type B	PVC/PVC

Isolation warning notice:

- Where live parts cannot be isolated by a single device, confirmation is required that a suitable warning notice is in place. The notice should be of durable material expected to last the life of the installation, and except where there is no possibility of confusion, the location of each isolator shall be indicated.

Periodic inspection and testing notice:

- Following the completion of the inspection and testing of an installation, a notice shall be fixed in a prominent position at the origin of the installation, which is usually the CU or DB front cover. The notice should be of durable material expected to last the life of the installation and give the date of the last inspection and recommended date of the next inspection. An example of NAPIT's notice is illustrated in Fig 7.6.

IMPORTANT

This installation should be periodically inspected and tested and a report on its condition obtained, as prescribed in the IET Wiring regulations BS 7671 Requirements for Electrical Installations.

NAPIT

Inspected by:

Date of last inspection:

Recommended date of next inspection:

Fig 7.6 Date of next inspection label

RCD six-monthly test notice:

- Where RCDs are installed, confirmation is needed that a notice has been fixed in a prominent position near each RCD in the installation. The notice provides details regarding six-monthly testing.

AFDD six-monthly test notice:

- Where AFDDs are installed, confirmation is needed that a notice has been fixed in a prominent position near each AFDD in the installation.

Warning notice of non-standard colours of conductor's present:

- Requires confirmation that there is a warning notice fixed to the appropriate CU/DB for installations with non-standard colours. Installations built before 2004 will typically be wired with a cable that has red and black coloured conductors, and newer installations will have conductors that are brown and blue in colour; see Fig 7.7 for clarification. When installations have been altered or extended, it is likely there will be a mixture of colours.

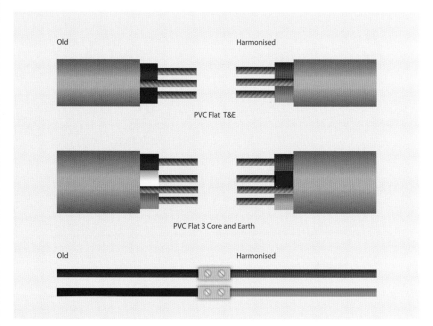

Fig 7.7 Identification of Conductors

- **7.11** requires confirmation that protective devices are suitably identified so that the circuit protected is easily recognised. In general, labels should be used to identify all switchgear and control gear, except where there is no possibility of confusion.

8.0 Circuits	
8.1	Adequacy of conductors for current-carrying capacity with regard to type and nature of the installation (Section 523)
8.2	Cable installation methods suitable for the location(s) and external influences (Section 522)
8.3	Segregation/separation of Band I (ELV) and Band II (LV) circuits, and electrical and non-electrical services (528)
8.4	Cables correctly erected and supported throughout with protection against abrasion (Sections 521, 522)
8.5	Provision of fire barriers, sealing arrangements where necessary (527.2)
8.6	Non-sheathed cables enclosed throughout in conduit, ducting or trunking (521.10.1; 526.8)
8.7	Cables concealed under floors, above ceilings or in walls/partitions, adequately protected against damage (522.6.201, 522.6.202, 522.6.203; 522.6.204)
8.8	Conductors correctly identified by colour, lettering or numbering (Section 514)
8.9	Presence, adequacy and correct termination of protective conductors (411.3.1.1; 543.1)
8.10	Cables and conductors correctly connected, enclosed and with no undue mechanical strain (Section 526)
8.11	No basic insulation of a conductor visible outside enclosure (526.8)
8.12	Single-pole devices for switching or protection in line conductors only (132.14.1; 530.3.3; 643.6)
8.13	Accessories not damaged, securely fixed, correctly connected, suitable for external influences (134.1.1; 512.2; Section 526)
8.14	**Provision of additional protection/requirements by RCD not exceeding 30 mA**
8.14.1	Socket-outlets rated at 32 A or less, unless exempt (411.3.3)
8.14.2	Supplies for mobile equipment with a current rating not exceeding 32 A for use outdoors (411.3.3)
8.14.3	Cables concealed in walls at a depth of less than 50 mm (522.6.202, 522.6.203)
8.14.4	Cables concealed in walls/partitions containing metal parts regardless of depth (522.6.202; 522.6.203)
8.14.5	Final circuits supplying luminaires within domestic (household) premises (411.3.4)

Fig 7.8 Extract of EIC inspection schedule sections 8 and 8.14

Inspection items 8.0 to 8.15: Circuits, see Fig 7.8

• **8.1** Requires confirmation that the current-carrying capacity of conductors is adequate with regards to the type and nature of the installation. The maximum operating temperatures for different types of cable are given in BS 7671 Section 523, Table 52.1. To ensure the maximum operating temperatures are not exceeded under normal operation, Inspectors will need to verify that the actual site conditions, reference methods, and cables used match what is stated in the design. The requirements are deemed to be met If the current does not exceed the values stated in the tables of current-carrying capacity given in BS 7671 Appendix 4 after applying any applicable rating factors and subject to Table 4A2, which provides a schedule of installation methods, reference methods for determining current-carrying capacity.

• **8.2** Requires confirmation that cable installation methods are appropriate for the location and expected external influences. The installation method, as well as the effects of external influence, should have been considered at the design stage. BS 7671 Appendix 5 gives the classification and coding of external influences. The designer of the electrical installation will need to consider the different seasons of the year and the resulting effects when selecting suitable equipment and wiring types. Inspectors will need to check everything is correct and in accordance with the design, with protection against the expected external influences in place throughout the wiring system. Examples of external influences to be considered are as follows:

  • Ambient temperature (AA)
  • External heat sources
  • Presence of water (AD)
  • Presence of high humidity (AB)
  • Presence of solid foreign bodies (AE)
  • Presence of corrosive polluting substances (AF)
  • Impact (AG)
  • Vibration (AH)
  • Mechanical stresses (AJ)
  • Presence of flora and/or mould growth (AK)
  • Presence of fauna (AL)
  • Solar radiation (AN) and ultraviolet radiation
  • Nature of processed or stored materials (BE)

- **8.3** Requires confirmation that there is adequate segregation/separation of extra-low voltage circuits (Band I) and low voltage circuits (Band II), and adequate segregation/separation of electrical and non-electrical services.

Inspectors will need to check that Band I and Band II circuits are not contained in the same wiring system unless one of the following methods is adopted:

- Every cable and conductor (including conductors of multi-core cables) is insulated for the highest voltage present
- Where cables are only insulated for their own system voltage, they may be segregated into separate compartments withing the cable trunking/ducting system
- Installed on cable tray with physical separation by a partition
- Separate wiring systems used
- Band I cores of a multi-core cable separated from Band II cores by an earthed metal screen that is capable of carrying the same level of current as the largest Band II conductor

Inspectors will also need to confirm adequate segregation/separation of electrical and non-electrical services. Where wiring systems are installed near services that could produce heat, smoke, or fumes, suitable protection (shielding) must be in place to prevent damage. Where any services capable of producing condensation such as water, steam, or gas services are routed above wiring systems, protection should be in place to protect against any harmful effects. Inspectors should assess the likelihood of damage to the wiring system caused by any foreseeable operation of the non-electrical service. If the suitable spacing is not in place, mechanical or thermal shielding will need to be in place. In all cases where an electrical service is in close proximity to one or more non-electrical services, protection must be in place to protect against any hazards likely to be introduced from the other service. Fault protection must meet the requirements of BS 7671 Section 411, i.e. protective earthing and bonding with ADS in case of a fault).

- **8.4** Requires confirmation that cables are correctly erected and supported throughout the installation, with adequate protection against abrasion. BS 7671 Table 4A1 Appendix 4 provides a schedule of installation methods in relation to conductors and cables. Where Inspectors are in doubt about a certain installation method, this schedule can be consulted to see what conductors and cables are permitted for each installation method. Inspectors will need to confirm the selection and erection of wiring systems are in accordance with BS 7671 Chapter 52 whilst taking into account the manufacturer's instructions. The quality of the workmanship shall be inspected to ensure there are no sharp edges, burrs, etc. that could cause abrasion issues; protection shall also be in place for any external influences likely to be present.

- **8.5** Requires confirmation that suitable sealing arrangements and fire barriers are in place, where wiring systems pass through elements of the building, such as floors, walls, ceilings, partitions, etc. The sealing arrangements need to meet the same level of fire resistance as provided by the building construction being penetrated; it shall:

  - Resist products of combustion to the same level
  - Provide the same degree of protection from water penetration
  - Compatible with the material of the wiring system in contact
  - Permit thermal movement of the wiring system
  - Provide adequate mechanical stability

See Fig 7.9, for an example of where fire stop blocks have been used to seal an opening penetrated by cable tray.

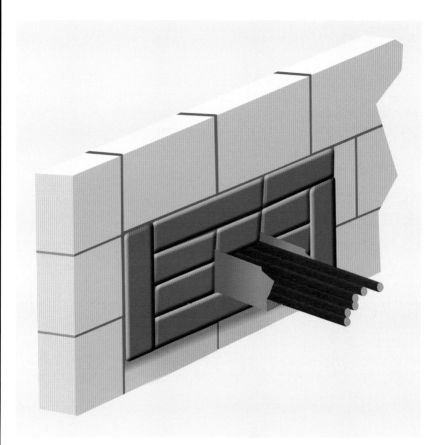

Fig 7.9 Fire barrier maintained using intumescent fire stopping blocks

Note

A conduit, trunking, or ducting system classified as non-flame propagating, having a maximum internal csa of 710 mm^2 need not be internally sealed (see Regulation 527.2.3 for full requirements). Therefore, small trunkings < 25 X 25 mm or conduits < 32 mm don't require internally sealing where they pass through a wall, remember they still require external sealing where they pass through. See Fig 7.10.

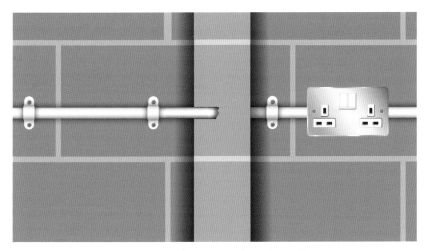

Fig 7.10 conduit passing through a wall

- **8.6** Requires confirmation that non-sheathed cables are enclosed throughout the installation in conduit, ducting, or trunking. However, this requirement does not apply to protective conductors installed in accordance with BS 7671 Section 543. The cable trunking system needs to have a degree of protection of at least IPXXD or IP4X with a cover that can only be removed by the use of a tool or deliberate action.

- **8.7** Concerns cables that are concealed under floors, above ceilings, or installed in walls or partitions. Inspectors need to ensure that there is adequate protection against any foreseeable damage.

- Cables run under floors or above ceilings should be installed, so they are not likely to be damaged by the floor or ceiling or their fixings. Cables passing through joists in ceilings or other ceiling supports shall:

- Be installed at least 50 mm from the top or bottom of the change to joist (whichever is relevant); see Fig 7.11.

  Or

- Comply with Regulation 522.6.204.

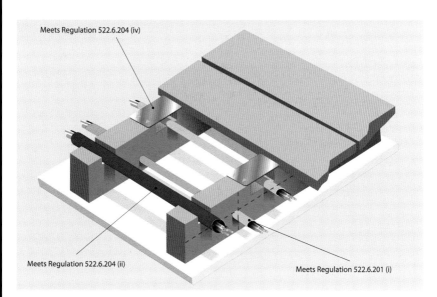

Meets Regulation 522.6.204 (iv)

Meets Regulation 522.6.204 (ii)

Meets Regulation 522.6.201 (i)

7.11 Impact requirements for notched and drilled joists

In order for cables to be protected from impact, any cables in walls or partitions shall:

- Be installed in safe zones, as described in Fig 7.12.

Or

- Comply with Regulation 522.6.204.

An extra requirement for Regulation 522.6.202 is where cables are installed in safe zones but do not comply with Regulation 522.6.204; they must be provided with an RCD not exceeding 30 mA for additional protection, in accordance with Regulation 415.1.1.

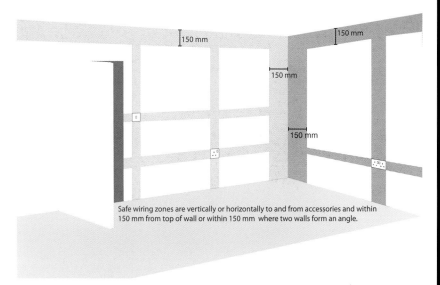

Safe wiring zones are vertically or horizontally to and from accessories and within 150 mm from top of wall or within 150 mm where two walls form an angle.

Fig 7.12 Safe wiring zones

Inspectors need to ensure that where any cables are buried within a metallic wall or partition with an internal metal construction, such as metal framed stud walls must:

- Be protected by an RCD not exceeding 30 mA in accordance with Regulation 415.1.1.

Or

- Comply with Regulation 522.6.204

Cables must also be installed in safe wiring zones, where they are less than 50 mm from the surface.

Where the method of protection has been to comply with Regulation 522.6.204 for any of the cable installation methods that have been discussed in this section, confirmation is required that one of the following options has been used:

1. Have an earthed covering and comply with BS 5467, BS 6724, BS 7846, BS 8436, or BS EN 60702-1

Or

215

2. Be contained in an earthed conduit (in accordance with BS EN 61386-21)

Or

3. Be contained in earthed ducting/trunking (in accordance with BS EN 50085-2-1)

Or

4. Have sufficient mechanical protection to withstand penetration from nails/screws, etc. (this mechanical protection does not require a connection to earth or the cpc of the circuit under protection)

Or

5. Be incorporated into a SELV or PELV circuit complying with Regulation 414.4

The option to use Regulation 522.6.204 is provided in the following Regulations and their respective sub-clauses:

- 522.6.201(ii)
- 522.6.202(ii)
- 522.6.203(ii)

- **8.8** Requires confirmation that conductors are correctly identified by colour, lettering, or numbering. Inspectors should check terminations throughout the installation to ascertain compliance. Regulation 514.6.1 permits identification of the following conductors or parts to be omitted:

  - Concentric conductors of cables
  - The metal sheath or armouring of a cable (where used as a PE)
  - Bare conductors
  - Extraneous-conductive-parts (where used as a PE)
  - Exposed-conductive-parts (where used as a PE)

For AC circuits, the alphanumeric and colour identification examples are given in Table 7.8

Table 7.8 Identification of AC conductors		
Conductor function	**Alphanumeric**	**Colour**
Protective conductors (PE)		Green-and-yellow
Functional earthing conductor		Pink
Line (single-phase)	L	Brown
Neutral (single or three-phase)	N	Blue
Line 1 (three-phase)	L1	Brown
Line 2 (three-phase)	L2	Black
Line 3 (three-phase)	L3	Grey

- **8.9** Requires verification of the presence, adequacy, and correct termination of protective conductors (PE). This means that all terminations to exposed-conductive-parts of the installation should be checked, as well as each point in the wiring system checked for the presence and correct termination of cpc. Lampholders with no exposed-conductive-parts suspended from the termination point are exempt from the requirements for protective earthing. Regulation 543.2.1 lists a number of different types of PE, as summarised below:

  - Single-core cables
  - A conductor in a multi-core cable
  - An insulated or bare conductor in a common enclosure, e.g., trunking
  - A metal covering, e.g., SWA armouring
  - Metallic cable management system, e.g. conduit
  - Exposed-conductive-parts (if compliant with Regulation 543.2.6)

- **8.10** Requires verification that cables and conductors are correctly connected and enclosed with no undue mechanical strain. The requirements for electrical connections are given in BS 7671 Section 526, with Regulation 526.1, making it very clear that 'every' connection must provide durable electrical continuity and adequate mechanical strength and protection. When assessing the adequacy of connections, inspectors will need to check or consider numerous requirements. The following list of questions is an example of what should be considered:

- Has the connection been made with good workmanship in accordance with the manufacturer's instructions?
- Is the terminal suited to the type and number of conductors?
- Are there locking arrangements for any terminations subject to vibration?
- Where multiwire or fine wire conductors have been used, have the conductor ends been fitted with suitable terminals?
- Is there sufficient protection against strain to any terminals or strain to the conductors themselves?
- Where terminations are made within an enclosure, does the enclosure provide adequate mechanical protection and protection against external influences likely to be present?

- **8.11** Requires inspection of enclosures to ensure no basic insulation of conductors is visible outside of the enclosure. When the sheath of the cable has been removed for its termination into equipment, inspectors need to confirm that the basic insulation is enclosed. Every termination of a live conductor must be made within a suitable accessory or equipment enclosure.

- **8.12** Requires verification that single-pole devices used for switching or protection are connected to line conductors only. Inspections should be made at all relevant points within the installation where CBs, fuses, or switches are installed. Confirmation that this requirement has been met is usually obtained during polarity testing, as required by Regulation 643.6(i).

- **8.13** Requires confirmation that accessories are suitably fixed and correctly connected with no damage. Accessories will need to be suitable for the external influences they will be subjected to. This requires inspectors to think about all the different conditions likely to be present when assessing the suitability. For example, when carrying out initial verification of equipment mounted outside in the summertime, as well as checking the equipment is suitable for the ambient temperature present, solar and UV, etc. You will also need to think about winter conditions (wind, rain, frost, and snow, etc.) when determining the suitability.

- **8.14** Requires verification that RCDs not exceeding 30 mA have been installed for additional protection/requirements; inspectors will need to check each of the following:

  - Have all socket-outlets rated at 32 A or less been provided with additional protection by RCDs not exceeding 30 mA? (unless exempt by Regulation 411.3.3, see note)

  - Have supplies to mobile equipment used outside with a current rating not exceeding 32 A been provided with additional protection by RCDs not exceeding 30 mA?

  - Have cables that have been installed in a wall at a depth of less than 50 mm been provided with additional protection by RCDs not exceeding 30 mA?

  - Where cables are installed in-wall/partitions containing metal parts, has additional protection by RCDs not exceeding 30 mA been provided?

  - Have all lighting circuits got additional protection by RCDs not exceeding 30 mA? (dwellings only)

Note

Regulation 411.3.3 permits additional protection by RCD not exceeding 30 mA to be omitted for socket-outlets in installations other than dwellings, providing a documented risk assessment determines that RCD protection is not necessary. The risk assessment will need to be available for scrutiny by the Inspector.

8.15	Presence of appropriate devices for isolation and switching correctly located including:
8.15.1	Means of switching off for mechanical maintenance (Section 464; 537.3.2)
8.15.2	Emergency switching (465.1; 537.3.3)
8.15.3	Functional switching, for control of parts of the installation and current-using equipment (463.1; 537.3.1)
8.15.4	Firefighter's switches (537.4)
9.0 Current-Using Equipment (Permanently Connected)	
9.1	Equipment not damaged, securely fixed and suitable for external influences (134.1.1; 416.2; 512.2)
9.2	Provision of overload and/or undervoltage protection e.g. for rotating machines, if required (Sections 445, 552)
9.3	Installed to minimize the build-up of heat and restrict the spread of fire (421.1.4; 559.4.1)
9.4	Adequacy of working space. Accessibility to equipment (132.12; 513.1)
10.0 Location(s) Containing A Bath Or Shower (Section 701)	
10.1	30 mA RCD protection for all LV circuits, equipment suitable for the zones, supplementary bonding (where required) etc.
11.0 Other Part 7 Special Installations or Locations (list all other special installations or locations present)	
11.1	List all other special installations or locations present, if any. (Record separately the results of particular inspections applied)
11.2	
11.3	
11.4	
11.5	

Fig 7.13 Extract of EIC inspection schedule sections 8.15, 9.0, 10.0 and 11.0

Inspection items 8.15 to 11.5, see Fig 7.13

- **8.15** Requires verification that appropriate devices have been installed for isolation and switching purposes and are correctly located. The following shall be considered:

Have means of switching off for mechanical maintenance been provided?

- Where provided, the switch must be capable of interrupting the full load current of the relevant part of the installation. The following devices are examples of devices suitable for switching off for mechanical maintenance:
- Multipole switch
- Circuit-breaker
- Control and switching device
- Control switch operating a contactor
- Plug and socket-outlet

Fig 7.14 Emergency Isolating switch

- Has means of emergency switching off, been provided for parts of the installation where it may be necessary to control the supply in order to remove unexpected danger?

  Where the risk is of an electrical nature, emergency switching must disconnect all live conductors unless the conditions of Regulation 461.2 apply. Any devices used for emergency switching shall be capable of interrupting the full load current of the relevant parts of the circuit whilst also considering any motor stalling current. The means of emergency switching off may be provided by a single device that deals with cutting off the relevant supply or may be provided by a combination of devices activated by a single action. Plug and socket-outlets are not appropriate for emergency switching off. Fig 7.14 shows a typical emergency switch with the preferred colour markings of red on a contrasting background of yellow. The device must be positioned readily accessible where danger may occur and be capable of latching in the 'off' position.

- Have means of functional switching been provided for control of parts of the installation and current using equipment?

  Where parts of a circuit are required to be controlled independently (such as lighting circuits), inspectors need to ensure adequate functional switching has been provided. Functional switching devices do not need to switch all live conductors and, therefore, can be single-pole devices but should not be connected in the neutral conductor unless permitted for lamp control circuits (see Regulation 463.1.2). Functional switching needs to be provided for current using equipment that requires control, where items of equipment operate simultaneously. They may be controlled via a single functional switching device.

- Where appropriate have firefighter's switches been installed?

  Firefighter's switches are usually installed in installations subject to licensing conditions, for example, petrol station forecourts. Where fitted, there are several requirements regarding positioning and labelling. The switch must be visible and accessible to firefighters, with the height of the switch (from the ground) not be more than 2.75 m. Full requirements are listed in Regulation 537.4

Inspection items 9.0 to 9.4: Current-using equipment (permanently connected)

- **9.1** Requires verification that equipment is not damaged, is correctly selected and erected, and suitable for the external influences likely to be present. Regulation 134.1.1 requires manufacturer's instructions to be taken into account, and therefore inspectors may need to obtain such information to ascertain compliance.

- **9.2** Requires verification of suitable overload protection and where rotating machines are installed, confirmation is required that provisions are provided for overload and/or under-voltage protection. For example, motors being provided with a means to prevent automatic restarting after a drop in voltage where the motor has stalled.

- **9.3** Requires verification that equipment is installed to minimize the build-up of heat and restrict the spread of fire. Where equipment produces a concentration of heat that is focused onto a surface, the distance should be sufficient to prevent detrimental effects. Where this cannot be achieved, extra measures may be needed, such as screening. Selection and erection should take account of the manufacturer's instructions; therefore, inspectors may need to obtain such information to ascertain compliance.

- **9.4** Requires confirmation that there is adequate accessibility to equipment with sufficient working space. Access is needed for:
  - Future equipment replacement
  - To allow correct operation
  - Inspection and testing
  - Fault finding
  - Maintenance
  - Repair

Inspection items 10.0 to 10.1: Locations containing a bath or shower (Section 701)

- **10.1** Requires verification that all LV circuits within the location are protected by RCDs not exceeding 30 mA and where required supplementary bonding has been installed correctly. All equipment must be appropriate for the zone where it is installed. As follows:

  - Equipment in zone 0 requires a minimum degree of protection of IPX7; no switchgear or accessories are permitted unless incorporated into fixed current-using equipment suitable for use in that zone. See Regulation 701.55 for full requirements.

  - Equipment in zone 1 requires a minimum degree of protection of IPX4, only switches of SELV circuits are permitted provided the safety source is installed outside of the zones. Only permanently connected equipment suitable for zone 1 (according to manufacturer's instructions) should be installed in zone 1.

- Equipment in zone 2 requires a minimum degree of protection of IPX4; only switches and socket-outlets of SELV circuits are permitted provided the safety source is installed outside of the zones. Shaver units to BS EN 61558-2-5 are also permitted.

Where equipment is exposed to water jets, protection should be to IPX5.

The above degrees of protection do not apply to shaver supply units complying with BS EN 61558-2-5 when installed in zone 2 if direct spray from showers is unlikely.

Inspection items 11.0 to 11.1: Other Part 7 special installations or locations

- **11.1** Requires the Inspector to list all other special installations or locations present and record the results separately. Not all Part 7s will be relevant, and therefore, it is down to the Inspector to include only the applicable inspections.

7.3 Electrical Installation Certificate (EIC)/Minor Electrical Installation Works Certificate (MEIWC)

Overall summary

Electrical Installation Certificates (EIC) are to be used for initial verification of new installations. Alternatively, they can be used for an addition or alteration to an existing installation where the level of work exceeds the amount that would normally be recorded on a Minor Electrical Installation Works Certificate (MEIWC). For example, where alterations involve multiple circuits or consumer unit replacements.

For new installations any defects or errors noted during the inspection and testing must be corrected prior to issuing the certificate.

For additions and alterations not requiring new circuits to be installed or where CU/DB replacements are not required, a MEIWC may be used.

Examples of model forms for EICs and MEIWCs can be found in Appendix 1 on page 275.

This page has been intentionally left blank

Section 8

Requirements for periodic inspection and testing

8.0 BS 7671:2018 Requirements for periodic inspection and testing

All electrical installations are subject to deterioration; this is quite normal; it happens with age, general wear and tear as they are used. Occasionally damage occurs from misuse of equipment or carelessness. Users of electrical installations may carry out works and modifications that may not meet the basic requirements for safety, as prescribed in the latest edition of BS 7671, which can lead to unsafe conditions. Likewise, a lack of or improper maintenance may compromise safety. Therefore, BS 7671 requires electrical installations to be periodically inspected and tested to ensure they are safe for continued use and to highlight areas of damage that may require rectification or upgrade.

The correct documentation for this purpose is the Electrical Installation Condition Report (EICR), which can be found in BS 7671 Appendix 6 and examples of which can also be found in Appendix 1 of this Guide.

8.1 Inspection and testing requirements

An inspection process always precedes any testing process, and BS 7671 states that only some dismantling may be required. It can be hazardous to dismantle all of the accessories in an installation on a regular basis, as they are generally not designed for this purpose, and doing so can damage them over time.

Dismantling should only be carried out with the permission of the Client, discussed later in this Section under 'Extent and Limitations – Agreed and Operational.' Extreme care must be taken when reinstating any dismantled equipment, where there is a possibility of incorporating a fresh fault in the reinstating process, when there may not have been a problem before dismantling.

The main objectives of the inspection are to confirm adequate protection against:

- Electric shock
- Electrical burns
- Damage to property by fire or heat from electrical installation defects

This will require confirmation that:

- The rating and setting of protective devices are correct (fuses/circuit-breakers/ Residual Current Devices (RCDs/RCBOs))
- The installation is not damaged or deteriorated
- No defects or non-compliances affecting electrical safety exist

The report shall include:

- Details of the parts of the installation that have been inspected and tested
- Any limitations of the inspection and testing
- Any damage, deterioration, defects, or dangerous conditions that exist
- Any non-compliances with regards to the requirements of BS 7671 which may give rise to danger
- Schedule of inspections
- Schedule of test results

Note

When reference is made to a report, this includes all of its constituent parts, which must include all of the limitations, observations, classification codes, individual inspection schedule(s), schedule(s) of test results and guidance to recipients, etc.

Where an EICR is being carried out under the Electrical Safety Standards in the Private Rented Sector (England) Regulations 2020, the Legislation calls for a report to be given to both the tenant and the person ordering the work. In both cases, it refers to the whole document and not a front sheet or similar. An example of the full required paperwork for an EICR can be found in Appendix 1 of this Guide.

8.1.1 Extent and Limitations – Agreed & Operational

Extent of the Inspection

When we refer to 'sampling' on an EICR, we are referring to the amount of circuits and accessories that are inspected or tested. This is important and should be discussed with the person ordering the work to confirm how much of the installation is to be inspected and tested, and how much is to be sampled and is called the extent of the inspection. This information is recorded in Section D of the EICR.

We should aim to inspect 100% of an installation unless there is a specific limitation placed on it.

When looking at the testing part of an EICR, the sampling process becomes more important. We should aim to test as many circuits as possible, close to 100%, unless limitations prevent this.

Where we are looking at accessories, we would perhaps sample 20% of the accessories on each circuit, and if regular damage was found, not just one-offs, more accessories should be inspected to confirm any issues. Remember, as previously mentioned, removing too many accessories can be detrimental, and BS 7671 only states that some dismantling may be necessary.

Agreed Limitation
As it suggests, a limitation is a part of the inspection procedure that should have been mutually agreed between the Inspector and the Client, or person ordering the work, before the inspection takes place. It denotes where a particular check or test is not carried out but is acceptable as it has been agreed prior to the Periodic inspection and testing starting.

An example of an agreed limitation may be for a large dwelling where there is no access to one of the outbuildings that is being used for storage. The limitation would be noted in the report, and the associated circuits/items within the outbuilding would not be inspected or tested as part of the EICR being carried out.

Likewise, in a commercial or industrial environment, an agreed limitation could be an area, room or process compartment that may be hazardous or not accessible unless significant controls are in place, which may prove impractical.

Unfortunately, the use of Limitations on EICRs is open to abuse. The person ordering the work should not limit the inspection for cost reasons alone, and only genuine limitations would be seen as appropriate by anyone scrutinising the report at a later date. Likewise, the person ordering the work should not allow the Inspector to limit inspection and testing without proper consideration.

Operational Limitation

As well as Agreed Limitations, there may also be Operational Limitations, which may need to be taken account of, such as:

- Communal locked area
- Secure locked area (e.g., a room in HMO, home office, legally held firearms and munitions, data storage area, hazardous materials compound, sensitive equipment compartment, etc.)
- Inaccessible equipment due to a lack of safe access, e.g., Lighting systems at extreme height, or enclosed compartments, etc.
- Workforce special shift patterns
- Tenant work patterns

Operational Limitations are very important and should be highlighted to the Landlord as they become apparent, as they may impact the EICR.

The Inspector may come across Operational Limitations during the inspection and testing that have not been pre-agreed, such as obstructions from furniture, deliveries of stock or raw materials, etc., these should be raised with the person ordering the work immediately and dealt with prior to the commencement of any further Inspections and Tests.

Where there is an agreed limitation in place, the EICR will highlight this with the classification 'Lim,' short for Limitation, and often denoted by the following symbol

8.1.2 Sampling vs Quality

Any sampling used on an EICR is a compromise against the amount of actual work that is carried out.

By applying excessive sampling to circuits, there is a risk of a low-quality EICR, as the inspection and any testing may not highlight hidden faults.

Oversampling of the same accessories on a regular basis can reduce the life of accessories through damage caused by their dismantling and reinstating, and the added possibility of introducing faults that weren't there previously.

If we do too little sampling of accessories, however, we run the risk of not seeing an accurate picture of an installation and its use.

There is a fine line between adequate sampling and maintaining a quality EICR. As each installation has a slightly different dynamic, it is vital that any sampling and requirements for quality are dealt with before the EICR commences.

8.2 Inspection schedule breakdown

8.2.1 Examples of items requiring inspection for an Electrical Installation Condition Report (EICR)

The process for periodic inspection is very different from initial verification; often, original design criteria and/or documentation from previous inspections are not available. Where it is available, it should be taken into account, but in most cases, investigation of the electrical installation will be needed prior to undertaking the EICR.

Existing installations may have been designed and installed to previous editions of BS 7671 and, therefore, will not comply with the current standard in every respect. This does not necessarily mean that they are unsafe for continued use or require an upgrade. Inspectors will need to apply engineering judgment when deciding what recommendations need to be made on the report. The classification code C3 is often used for such instances apart from where the Inspector feels strongly about the need to upgrade based on safety reasons, for example, where cables are liable to premature collapse in a fire and may cause entanglement, and in this case, a C2 would be appropriate.

BS 7671 Appendix 6 provides a model EICR inspection domestic and similar premises with up to 100 A supply. The following is a breakdown of EICR inspection schedules using NAPIT model forms.

Description of EICR Schedule Items

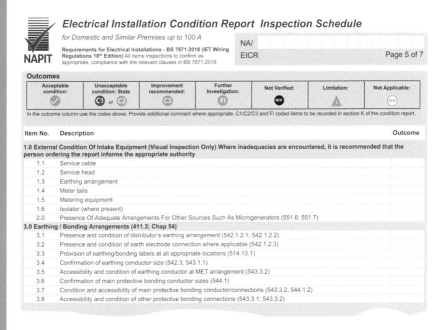

Electrical Installation Condition Report Inspection Schedule

for Domestic and Similar Premises up to 100 A

Requirements for Electrical Installations - BS 7671:2018 (IET Wiring Regulations 18th Edition) All items inspections to confirm as appropriate, compliance with the relevant clauses in BS 7671:2018

NA/

EICR

Page 5 of 7

Outcomes

Acceptable condition:	Unacceptable condition: State	Improvement recommended:	Further Investigation:	Not Verified:	Limitation:	Not Applicable:
✓	C1 or C2	C3	FI	N/V	⚠	N/A

In the outcome column use the codes above. Provide additional comment where appropriate. C1/C2/C3 and FI coded items to be recorded in section K of the condition report.

Item No.	Description	Outcome
1.0 External Condition Of Intake Equipment (Visual Inspection Only) Where inadequacies are encountered, it is recommended that the person ordering the report informs the appropriate authority		
1.1	Service cable	
1.2	Service head	
1.3	Earthing arrangement	
1.4	Meter tails	
1.5	Metering equipment	
1.6	Isolator (where present)	
2.0	Presence Of Adequate Arrangements For Other Sources Such As Microgenerators (551.6; 551.7)	
3.0 Earthing / Bonding Arrangements (411.3; Chap 54)		
3.1	Presence and condition of distributor's earthing arrangement (542.1.2.1; 542.1.2.2)	
3.2	Presence and condition of earth electrode connection where applicable (542.1.2.3)	
3.3	Provision of earthing/bonding labels at all appropriate locations (514.13.1)	
3.4	Confirmation of earthing conductor size (542.3; 543.1.1)	
3.5	Accessibility and condition of earthing conductor at MET arrangement (543.3.2)	
3.6	Confirmation of main protective bonding conductor sizes (544.1)	
3.7	Condition and accessibility of main protective bonding conductor/connections (543.3.2; 544.1.2)	
3.8	Accessibility and condition of other protective bonding connections (543.3.1; 543.3.2)	

Fig 8.1 Extract of EICR inspection schedule, Sections 1 to 3

Inspection Items 1.0 to 1.6: External condition of intake equipment (visual inspection only), see Fig 8.1

This section of the inspection schedule is dedicated to the condition of the intake equipment. The equipment in this area of the installation is owned by the DNO and the meter operator; therefore, the Inspector does not have permission to undertake an intrusive inspection. Comments and outcomes can only be based on the results of visual inspection of the external condition.

A visual inspection will include looking for any mechanical damage or signs of thermal damage to the equipment. Meter tails and protective earthing conductor sizes should be verified to ensure they are sufficient for the installation's maximum demand and earthing requirements. The health of cable insulation can be verified to ensure there is no mechanical damage and no signs of overloading, thermal damage, cracks, or splits to the insulation.

The adequacy of any cabling support can also be verified to ensure there is no strain on the conductors or associated terminals.

Inspection Item 2.0: Presence of adequate arrangements for other sources such as microgenerators

This inspection item concerns installations where generating sets are operating either:

- In parallel to the public supply (such as solar PV), or
- Operating as an alternative to the public supply (such as a standby generator).

Where installations contain alternative sources of supply, Inspectors will need to confirm the requirements listed in Chapter 55 of BS 7671 are met. Where the generator set is used as a switched alternative to the public supply, suitable precautions are required to prevent the generator from running in parallel to the public supply. Inspectors should check that the relevant parts of Chapter 46 and Section 537 regarding isolation have been complied with. See Regulation 551.6 for further guidance.

Where the generator set operates in parallel to the public supply, Inspectors will need to ensure the following conditions are met:

- Protection against thermal effects (Chapter 42) and protection against overcurrent (Chapter 43) shall remain effective in all situations
- Where additional protection is provided an RCD not exceeding 30 mA, for the generator circuit, the RCD must disconnect all live conductors, including the neutral conductor. See Regulation 551.7.1 for further guidance.

Inspection Items 3.0 to 3.8: Earthing/Bonding arrangements

- **3.1** Inspectors will need to confirm the presence and condition of the distributors earthing arrangement:
    - For TN-S systems, confirmation is required that there is an adequate connection between the Distributor's earth (which is usually the cable sheath) and the installations MET, as required by Regulation 542.1.2.1
    - For TN-C-S systems, confirmation is required that there is an adequate connection between the neutral of the source of supply and the installations MET, as required by Regulation 542.1.2.2.

- **3.2** Inspectors will need to confirm the presence and condition of the earth electrode connection where applicable. For TT or IT systems, confirmation is required that there is an adequate connection between the earth electrode and the installations MET, as required by Regulation 542.1.2.3.

- **3.3** Provision of earthing/bonding labels at all appropriate locations: Regulation 514.13.1 requires durable labels to be permanently fixed in a noticeable position at:

  1. Earthing conductor connection points, including connections to earth electrodes, and

  2. Bonding conductor connection points to extraneous-conductive-parts, and

  3. The MET, where separate from the main switchgear

The label should read 'Safety Electrical Connection – Do Not Remove,' see Fig 7.3.

- **3.4** Inspectors will need to confirm the size of the earthing conductor:

  - Confirmation that the size of the installed earthing conductor meets minimum requirements with electrically and mechanically sound connections. Connections and joints should be accessible as required by Regulation 543.2.

  - Confirmation of adequate earthing conductor csa in accordance with Table 8.1. Where the csa is less than required by Table 8.2 the adiabatic equation may be used in accordance with Regulation 543.1.3.

Where the earthing conductor has been buried in the ground, the minimum csa should be in accordance with BS 7671 Table 54.1, a representation of this can be seen in Table 8.1.

Table 8.1 Minimum cross-sectional area of protective conductor in relation to the cross-sectional area of associated line conductor

Cross-sectional area of line conductor S	Minimum cross-sectional area of the protective conductor (with reference to the line conductor)	
	Where protective conductor and line conductor material are the same	Where protective conductor and line conductor material are different
(mm²)	(mm²)	(mm²)
Where S is less than or equal to 16	S	$\dfrac{k_1}{k_2} \times S$
Where S is greater than 16 but less than or equal to 35	16	$\dfrac{k_1}{k_2} \times 16$
Where S is greater than 35	$\dfrac{S}{2}$	$\dfrac{k_1}{k_2} \times \dfrac{S}{2}$

Were: k_1 is the value of k for the line conductor, selected from Table 43.1 in Chapter 43 of BS 7671 according to the materials of both conductor and insulation. k_2 is the value of k for the protective conductor, selected from Tables 54.2, 54.3, 54.4, 54.5 and 54.6 of BS 7671 as applicable.

Table 8.2 BS 7671 54.1 minimum csa of a buried earthing conductor

Earthing conductor	Earthing conductor protected against mechanical damage	Earthing conductor not protected against mechanical damage
Protection against corrosion (sheathed conductor)	2.5 mm² copper 10 mm² steel	16 mm² copper 16 mm² coated steel
No protection against corrosion (bare conductor)	25 mm² copper 50 mm² steel	25 mm² copper 50 mm² steel

- **3.5** Concerns accessibility and condition of the earthing conductor at the MET, Regulation 543.3.2 requires every connection and joint to be accessible for inspection, testing, and maintenance apart from joints designed to be buried or maintenance-free (see Regulation 526.3).

- **3.6** Inspectors will need to confirm the size of the main bonding conductor:

  - For TN-S and TT supplies, the conductor csa shall not be less than half the csa required for the Earthing conductor of the installation and must not be less than 6 mm², see Table 8.3. The minimum csa for main protective bonding conductors for PME supplies shall be selected in accordance with BS 7671 Table 54.8, summarised below in Table 8.4.

Note:

PME protective bonding is sized in relation to the PEN conductor and can result in larger conductors being required.

Table 8.3 Protective bonding sizes for TN-S and TT supplies

TN-S and TT supplies		
csa of Line conductor mm²	csa of Earthing conductor mm²	csa of Protective bonding conductor mm²
16	16	10
25	16	10
35	16	10
50	25	16
70	35	25*

*The csa need not exceed 25 mm² if copper or equivalent conductance

Table 8.4 TN-C-S (PME) Protective bonding conductor sizes

Copper equivalent csa of the PEN conductor	csa of Protective bonding conductor
35 or less	10
over 35 up to 50	16
over 50 up to 95	25
over 95 up to 150	35
over 150	50

- **3.7** Concerns the accessibility and condition of main bonding conductor connections:

    - Connections and joints should be accessible as required by Regulation 543.3.2 with electrically and mechanically sound connections. All extraneous-conductive-parts within the installation should be connected to the installations MET, as required by Regulation 411.3.1.2, and therefore confirmation is required for all bonded parts.

- **3.8** Concerns the accessibility and condition of supplementary protective bonding connections.

4.0 Consumer Unit(s) / Distribution Board(s)	
4.1	Adequacy of working space/accessibility to consumer unit/distribution board (132.12; 513.1)
4.2	Security of fixing (134.1.1)
4.3	Condition of enclosure(s) in terms of IP rating, etc. (416.2)
4.4	Condition of enclosure(s) in terms of fire rating, etc. (421.1.201; 526.5)
4.5	Enclosure not damaged/deteriorated so as to impair safety (651.2)
4.6	Presence of main linked switch (as required by 462.1.201)
4.7	Operation of main switches (functional check) (643.10)
4.8	Manual operation of circuit-breakers and RCD(s) to prove disconnection (643.10)
4.9	Correct identification of circuit details and protective devices (514.8.1; 514.9.1)
4.10	Presence of RCD six-monthly test notice at or near consumer unit/distribution board (514.12.2)
4.11	Presence of non-standard (mixed) cable colour warning notice at or near consumer unit/distribution board (514.14)
4.12	Presence of alternative supply warning notice at or near consumer unit/distribution board (514.15)
4.13	Presence of other required labelling (please specify) (Section 514)
4.14	Compatibility of protective devices, bases and other components; correct type and rating (no signs of unacceptable thermal damage, arcing or overheating) (411.3.2; 411.4; 411.5; 411.6; section 432.433)
4.15	Single-pole switching or protective devices in line conductor only (132.14.1; 530.3.3)
4.16	Protection against mechanical damage where cables enter consumer unit/distribution board (132.14.1; 522.8.1; 522.8.5; 522.8.11)
4.17	Protection against electromagnetic effects where cables enter consumer unit/distribution board/enclosures (521.5.1)
4.18	RCD(s) provided for fault protection - includes RCBOs (411.4.204; 411.5.2; 531.2)
4.19	RCD(s) provided for additional protection/requirements - includes RCBOs (411.3.3; 415.1)
4.20	Confirmation of indication that SPD is functional (651.4)
4.21	Confirmation that ALL conductor connections, including connections to busbars, are correctly located in terminals and are tight and secure (526.1)
4.22	Adequate arrangements where a generating set operates as a switched alternative to the public supply (551.6)
4.23	Adequate arrangements where a generating set operates in parallel with the public supply (551.7)

Fig 8.2 Extract of EICR inspection schedule, Sections 4.0 to 4.23

Inspection Items 4.0 to 4.23: Consumer unit(s)/distribution boards, see Fig 8.2

- **4.1** Concerns the adequacy of working space and access to consumer units (CU), distribution boards (DB). Regulation 132.12 requires sufficient space for the initial installation but also for future replacements. All equipment must be accessible for operation, maintenance, inspection and testing, and repair. Where no access is possible, e.g., where the CU/DB is obstructed by a fitted kitchen or cupboard, etc. it is likely that the outcome of the inspection will be unsatisfactory, with a C2 classification code used. Where access to the CU/DB is partially blocked, e.g., by storage materials, etc. then it is likely the outcome will be satisfactory with a recommendation for improvement code C3.

- **4.2** Concerns the security of fixings. Inspectors will need to ensure the CU/DB has solid fixings and is secure to the wall, basically checking that it was installed by good workmanship using proper materials.

- **4.3** Concerns the condition of the CU/DB enclosure in terms of IP rating. Where barriers or enclosures are used to prevent contact with live parts, the minimum degree of protection should be IPXXB or IP2X. IP2X equates to a hole size of 12.5 mm in diameter, which is deemed suitable to prevent contact with live parts with a finger. Regulation 416.2.1 advises of situations where larger openings are necessary for the proper functioning of equipment or to replace parts, suitable precautions shall be taken. The horizontal top surface of the CU/DB must have a minimum degree of protection of at least IPXXD or IP4X. IP4X equates to a hole size of 1 mm in diameter, which is deemed suitable to prevent contact with live parts with a wire.

- **4.4** Concerns the condition of the CU/DB enclosure(s) for fire ratings, the materials used for the enclosure will have to comply with the resistance of heat and fire requirements of a suitable product standard. The materials need to withstand the highest temperature produced by the electrical equipment that will be present during normal conditions. For domestic installations, Regulation 421.1.201 requires non-combustible enclosures for consumer units and similar switchgear. Alternatively, the consumer unit or switchgear can be enclosed in a non-combustible cabinet or enclosure, providing access is not restricted. This prevents the spread of electrical fires should one start within the unit. This does not mean that plastic consumer units are unsafe, but it means Inspectors will need to assess their suitability for continued use based on a number of factors, such as the condition, signs of thermal damage, etc.

- **4.5** Also concerns the condition of the enclosure; inspection is required to see if there are any defects or deterioration that could be a safety breach. The enclosure acts as a barrier to prevent electric shock and burns.

- **4.6** Requires confirmation that each electrical installation has a main linked switch or linked circuit-breaker at the origin for switching and isolation purposes. For single-phase supplies to CUs that will be operated by ordinary persons, the main switch must interrupt both live conductors as required by Regulation 462.1.201.

- **4.7** Requires manual operation of the main switch (functional testing) to ensure correct operation and confirm that switching off actually isolates the supply. The presence of voltage should be tested with approved test equipment, as listed in Section 5.

- **4.8** Requires manual operation of circuit-breakers and RCDs (functional testing) to ensure correct operation and prove disconnection. The presence of voltage should be tested with approved test equipment, as listed in Section 5.

- **4.9** Requires confirmation of the correct identification of circuit details and protective devices so that they are easily recognised. A requirement of BS 7671 is for a chart or diagram to be provided with extra details, and this should be in or adjacent to the CU/DB. Confirmation is required that a legible diagram, chart, or table or equivalent form of information is provided within or adjacent to the CU or DB. Indicating in particular:

- The type and composition of each circuit
- Points of utilisation served
- Number and size of conductors
- Type of wiring
- The method used for compliance with Regulation 410.3.2, which requires that protective measures shall consist of an appropriate combination of a provision for basic protection and independent provision for fault protection. Alternatively, an enhanced protective measure may be used, which provides both basic and fault protection, such as reinforced insulation.
- Information needed for the identification of devices providing protection, isolation, and switching
- Circuits or equipment vulnerable to electrical testing

- **4.10** Requires confirmation that where RCDs are installed, a notice has been fixed in a prominent position near each RCD in the installation. The notice provides details regarding six-monthly testing.

- **4.11** Requires confirmation that there is a warning notice for installations with non-standard colours. Installations built prior to 2004 will typically be wired with a cable that has red and black/red,yellow, blue and black coloured conductors, and newer installations will have conductors that are brown and blue/brown, black, grey and blue in colour. When installations have been altered or extended, it is likely there will be a mixture of colours. Where this is the case, there is a requirement to label the CU/DB to indicate that great care is needed before carrying out work, Fig 8.3

CAUTION

This installation has wiring colours to two versions of BS 7671.
Great care should be taken before undertaking extension, alteration or repair that all conductors are correctly identified.

Fig 8.3 Warning Notice: Non-standard colours

- **4.12** Requires confirmation that any installations with an alternative or additional source of supply (such as solar PV) have suitable warning notices at the CU/DB position. See example label, Fig 8.4.

WARNING
dual supply

Do not work on this equipment until it is isolated from both the mains and on-site generation supplies

Isolate on-site generator at _____

Isolate mains supply _____

Fig 8.4 Dual supply warning label

- **4.13** This item is for any additional warning notices that may be required; Inspectors will need to detail. For example, there are more onerous requirements to label installations with solar PV, and therefore Inspectors will need to check the requirements of Section 712 of BS 7671 and note this against this inspection item. See the example label, Fig 8.5, regarding PV DC junction boxes.

PV array DC junction box Danger - contains live parts during daylight

Fig 8.5 PV array junction box warning label

- **4.14** Concerns the compatibility of protective devices and consumer unit components. When consumer units are originally tested by their manufacturer, they are tested to ensure all components are compatible. If another manufacturer's product is introduced as part of an alteration, then the Inspector will need to look closely at this alteration. It is doubtful that the original consumer unit manufacturer would support the alteration, and therefore it will have to be assessed on its own merits. If any signs of thermal damage, arcing or overheating are evident, the inspection outcome will be unsatisfactory, with a **C2** classification code used. If there are none of these signs and the enclosure has not been modified to fit the equipment, everything looks fine, and the only issue is mixed branding, then it is likely the Inspector will make a recommendation for improvement, Code **C3**

- **4.15** Requires confirmation that single-pole devices used for switching or protection are connected to line conductors only. Inspections should be made at all relevant points within the installation where CBs, fuses, or switches are installed. Confirmation that this requirement has been met is usually obtained during polarity testing, as required by Regulation 643.6(i).

- **4.16** Requires confirmation that adequate protection is in place to prevent mechanical damage to cable sheaths and insulation, where cables enter the CU/DB. The inspection will include that there are no sharp edges on any cable supports or enclosures, therefore preventing damage during installation, use, or maintenance. This is especially important for metal enclosures with sharp edges. Because of the need to seal the hole appropriately (inspection item 4.3), suitable glands are often used but are not mandatory, as long as there is protection against abrasion. Protection could simply be from a rubber grommet. See Fig 8.6 for an example of a meter tail entry gland.

Fig 8.6 Meter tail entry gland

- **4.17** To avoid the build-up of circulating currents (eddy currents) and the effects of heat in ferromagnetic enclosures. Confirmation is required that all line conductors, neutral conductors, and associated protective conductors enter through the same hole. Where this is not achievable, they may enter through individual holes with slots cut between them (providing the integrity of the IP rating is not compromised).

- **4.18** The next two items refer to Residual Current Device (RCDs) and Residual Current Circuit-breaker with Overcurrent protection (RCBOs). RCD has become a generic term for many devices capable of operation when subjected to a predetermined value. Where RCDs are used for fault protection, they may have various sensitivity ratings, depending on the application. Inspectors will need to verify that the type and rating are appropriate for the installation, and the device is functioning correctly.

- **4.19** Inspectors will need to confirm the presence and effectiveness of RCDs provided for additional protection. Where RCDs with a current rating not exceeding 30 mA are used for additional protection in accordance with Regulation 415.1. Inspectors will need to ensure the device is of the correct type and rating and functioning correctly in order to be effective in the event of failure of basic protection and/or fault protection. Various Regulations require the use of 30 mA RCDs for life protection and to protect against the carelessness of users.

- **4.20** Requires confirmation that where surge protective devices (SPDs) are fitted, that they have indication that they are functional. SPDs are used to protect the installation from overvoltages; these can be from the effects of lightning or from switching activities. These devices have status indicating windows that change colour if they become defective, usually turning from green to red when they need replacement, see Fig 8.7.

Fig 8.7 SPD with a status indicating window

- **4.21** Requires confirmation that all conductor connections are correctly located in their respective terminals and are tight and secure in order to provide durable electrical continuity and suitable mechanical strength. For successful terminations, it is essential that the manufacturer's instructions are taken into account regarding the type and number of conductors suited to each terminal. Where cables are disturbed for testing purposes, they will need to be re-terminated and torqued appropriately using manufacturers' literature.

- **4.22** Requires confirmation that there are adequate arrangements for any installations where a generating set operates as a switched alternative to the public supply. Suitable measures must in place to prevent the generator from running in parallel to the public supply. A three-position 'break-before-make' changeover switch is an example of a suitable arrangement.

- **4.23** Requires confirmation that there are adequate arrangements for any installations where a generating set operates in parallel with the public supply. Inspectors will need to confirm that the installation has not compromised safety in any way and is not causing any adverse effects on the installation.

5.0 Final Circuits	
5.1	Identification of conductors (514.3.1)
5.2	Cables correctly supported throughout their run (521.10.202; 522.8.5)
5.3	Condition of insulation of live parts (416.1)
5.4	Non-sheathed cables protected by enclosure in conduit, ducting or trunking. Integrity of containment (521.10.1)
5.4.1	To include the integrity of conduit and trunking systems (metallic and plastic)
5.5	Adequacy of cables for current-carrying capacity with regard for the type and nature of installation (Section 523)
5.6	Coordination between conductors and overload protective devices (433.1; 533.2.1)
5.7	Adequacy of protective devices: type and rated current for fault protection (411.3)
5.8	Presence and adequacy of circuit protective conductors (433.3.1; Section 543)
5.9	Wiring system(s) appropriate for the type and nature of the installation and external influences (Section 522)
5.10	Concealed cables installed in prescribed zones (see Section D. Extent and limitations) (522.6.202)
5.11	Cables concealed under floors, above ceilings or in walls/partitions, adequately protected against damage (see Section D. Extent and limitations) (522.6.204)
5.12	**Provision of additional requirements for protection by RCD not exceeding 30 mA**
5.12.1	For all socket-outlets of rating 32 A or less, unless an exception is permitted (411.3.3)
5.12.2	For the supply of mobile equipment not exceeding 32 A rating for use outdoors (411.3.3)
5.12.3	For cables concealed in walls at a depth of less than 50 mm (522.6.202; 522.6.203)
5.12.4	For cables concealed in walls/partitions containing metal parts regardless of depth (522.6.203)
5.12.5	For circuits supplying luminaires within domestic (household) premises (411.3.4)
5.13	Provision of fire barriers, sealing arrangements and protection against thermal effects (Section 527)
5.14	Band II cables segregated/separated from Band I cables (528.1)
5.15	Cables segregated/separated from communications cabling (528.2)
5.16	Cables segregated/separated from non-electrical services (528.3)
5.17	**Termination of cables at enclosures - indicate extent of sampling in Section D of the report (Section 526)**
5.17.1	Connections soundly made and under no undue strain (526.6)
5.17.2	No basic insulation of a conductor visible outside enclosure (526.8)
5.17.3	Connections of live conductors adequately enclosed (526.5)
5.17.4	Adequately connected at point of entry to enclosure (glands, bushes, etc.) (522.8.5)
5.18	Condition of accessories including socket-outlets, switches and joint boxes (651.2(v))
5.19	Suitability of accessories for external influences (512.2)
5.20	Adequacy of working space/accessibility to equipment (132.12; 513.1)
5.21	Single-pole switching or protective devices in line conductors only (132.14.1, 530.3.3)

Fig 8.8 Extract of EICR inspection schedule section 5

Inspection Items 5.0 to 5.21: Final circuits, see Fig 8.8

- **5.1** Requires confirmation of conductor identification, every core of every cable must be correctly identified at its terminations and throughout its length. Cables can be identified by colour, letters, or numbers.

- **5.2** Concerns cable support, and there are two aspects to consider. Firstly, Inspectors will need to check that no cables are unsupported, causing strain on terminations or strain to the actual cable itself. In recent years it has become a requirement for meter tails to also be included in this check; see the note in Regulation 522.8.6. The second aspect is not an electrical safety issue but an entanglement issue. During a fire, the temperature rise can cause plastic supports such as clips, cleats, and cable ties, PVC trunking, and conduit systems to collapse. The cables will possibly hang down and create an entanglement hazard, which may hinder evacuation and firefighting activities. For any cables or wiring systems not adequately supported against premature collapse, where the collapse could cause entanglement, the outcome of the inspection will be a Code C2, therefore unsatisfactory. See Fig 8.9 for an example of metallic support added inside plastic trunking to protect against a premature collapse in the event of a fire.

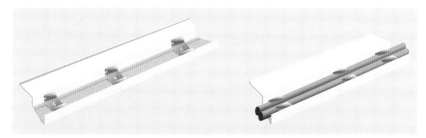

Fig 8.9 Cable support complying with premature collapse requirements

- **5.3** Concerns the condition of insulation of live parts, covered by insulation, where it was provided, to prevent contact with them to prevent contact with them. Conductors must be fully covered with durable insulation that can only be removed by destruction as required by Regulation 416.1. For equipment, insulation providing basic protection will need to meet the product standard of that equipment.

- **5.4** Requires confirmation that non-sheathed cables are protected by an enclosure, in conduit, ducting, or trunking. For cables to be installed outside of an enclosure, they need to be insulated and sheathed cables, e.g., like an appliance cable or extension lead. When the outer sheath is removed, the inner cores are now exposed with only single insulation. Inspectors should check all junction boxes, light fittings, etc. to see that no single insulation (basic insulation) is exposed. Whilst this check is carried out, where applicable, Inspectors shall also confirm the integrity of any conduit or trunking systems installed.

- **5.5** Requires confirmation that all cables are correctly sized for the intended purpose. Cables must be sized according to the load after considering a number of other factors; inspectors will need to ensure they are adequately sized for their application.

- **5.6** A further check from the previous one is to ensure there is correct coordination between conductors and the protective device. Confirmation is required that the current-carrying capacity of conductors is adequate with regards to the type and nature of the installation. The maximum operating temperatures for different types of cable are given in BS 7671 Section 523, Table 52.1. To ensure the maximum operating temperatures are not exceeded under normal operation, Inspectors will need to verify that the actual site conditions, reference methods, and cables used are suitable. The requirements are deemed to be met If the current does not exceed the values stated in the tables of current-carrying capacity given in BS 7671 Appendix 4 after applying any applicable rating factors and subject to Table 4A2, which provides a schedule of installation methods, reference methods for determining current-carrying capacity.

- **5.7** The previous check was with concerns to protection against overloading cables. This item regards checking the protective device is rated correctly for fault conditions. Inspectors will need to ensure that disconnection times can be met in order to achieve ADS; therefore, this will also require confirmation that the earthing arrangements are suitable for the particular type of system. Where protective devices are providing protection against both overload and fault current (which is the usual arrangement in most cases), the device must be capable of breaking any overcurrent up to the maximum prospective fault current (I_{pf}) at the point where the device is installed. Additionally, circuit-breakers must also be able to make the circuit under these conditions. Regulation 434.5.1 requires the rated short-circuit breaking capacity of each protective device shall not be less than the maximum I_{pf} at the point where the device is installed. There is an exception to this, where devices with a lower-rated breaking capacity are backed up by a device installed on the supply side that has the necessary rated short-circuit breaking capacity. In such cases, it may be necessary to check the manufacturer's technical data to ensure the energy let-through level does not exceed the level which can be withstood without damage by the lower-rated device on the load side.

- **5.8** Requires confirmation that each point of the wiring system has a circuit protective conductor (CPC) present. The only exception to this is for the final cable drop to a non-metallic lamp holder.

- **5.9** Requires confirmation that wiring systems are fit for purpose after considering the environment where they are installed. Inspectors will need to check everything is correct and in accordance with the design, with protection against the expected external influences in place throughout the wiring system. Examples of external influences to be considered are as follows:

  - Ambient temperature (AA)
  - External heat sources
  - Presence of water (AD)
  - Presence of high humidity (AB)
  - Presence of solid foreign bodies (AE)
  - Presence of corrosive polluting substances (AF)
  - Impact (AG)
  - Vibration (AH)
  - Mechanical stresses (AJ)
  - Presence of flora and/or mould growth (AK)
  - Presence of fauna (AL)
  - Solar radiation (AN) and ultraviolet radiation
  - Nature of processed or stored materials (BE)

- **5.10** Concerns concealed cables, installed in prescribed zones. A study of Fig 8.10 will show the prescribed zones (safe zones). The idea behind safe wiring zones is that no cables are buried anywhere you wouldn't expect them to be, thus preventing accidents from anyone drilling the wall, perhaps hanging a picture. Section D of the report contains a standard script stating that concealed cables have not been inspected unless specifically agreed between the client and Inspector, and therefore, this may fall outside of the EICR.

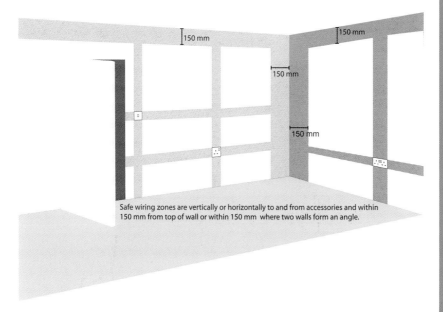

Safe wiring zones are vertically or horizontally to and from accessories and within 150 mm from top of wall or within 150 mm where two walls form an angle.

Fig 8.10 Prescribed (safe) wiring zones

- **5.11** Concerns cables concealed under floors, above ceilings, or in walls are adequately protected against damage. As stated in the previous item, this may fall outside of the scope of the EICR. Inspectors need to ensure that there is adequate protection against any foreseeable damage. Cables run under floors or above ceilings should be installed, so they are not likely to be damaged by the floor or ceiling or their fixings. Cables passing through joists in ceilings or other ceiling supports shall:

Be installed at least 50 mm from the top or bottom of the said joist (whichever is relevant)

Or

Comply with Regulation 522.6.204

Where the method of protection has been to comply with Regulation 522.6.204 for any of the cable installation methods that have been discussed in this section, confirmation is required that one of the following options has been used:

1. Have an earthed covering and comply with BS 5467, BS 6724, BS 7846, BS 8436 or BS EN 60702-1

   Or

2. Be contained in an earthed conduit (in accordance with BS EN 61386-21)

   Or

3. Be contained in earthed ducting/trunking (in accordance with BS EN 50085-2-1)

   Or

4. Have sufficient mechanical protection to withstand penetration from nails/screws, etc. (this mechanical protection does not require a connection to earth or the cpc of the circuit under protection)

   Or

5. Be incorporated into a SELV or PELV circuit complying with Regulation 414.4

The option to use Regulation 522.6.204 is provided in the following Regulations and their respective sub-clauses:

- 522.6.201(ii)
- 522.6.202(ii)
- 522.6.203(ii)

- **5.12** Provides a list of requirements regarding not exceeding 30 mA RCDs; inspectors will need to check each of the following:
   - Have all socket-outlets rated at 32 A or less been provided with additional protection by RCD not exceeding 30 mA? Unless an exception is permitted by a risk assessment for buildings other than dwellings, see Regulation 411.3.3
   - Have supplies to any mobile equipment rated at 32 A or less which is used outside been provided with additional protection by RCD not exceeding 30 mA RCD?

- Have cables installed in a wall at a depth of less than 50 mm got additional protection by RCD not exceeding 30 mA?
- Where cables are installed in-wall/partitions containing metal parts, has additional protection been provided?
- Have all lighting circuits, in dwellings got additional protection by RCD not exceeding 30 mA?

- **5.13** Requires checks on the adequacy of any fire barriers, sealing arrangements, and protection against thermal effects. Where wiring systems pass through floors, walls, roofs, ceilings, etc. the openings should be sealed to minimize the spread of fire. Further investigation may be required to assess the sealing arrangements to ensure they maintain the same level of fire resistance as provided by the building construction being penetrated; check if:
  - Resist products of combustion to the same level
  - Provide the same degree of protection from water penetration
  - Compatible with the material of the wiring system in contact
  - Permit thermal movement of the wiring system
  - Provide adequate mechanical stability

- **5.14** Concerns the segregation of Band I and Band II cables. 230 V mains powered cables are classed as Band II, with Telecommunications, signaling, control, and alarm cables being considered as Band I. Inspectors will need to check that where a mixture of these exist, they are kept separate unless certain conditions exist, for example, every cable or conductor present will require insulation rated for the highest voltage present.

- **5.15** Concerns the segregation of communications cabling where power cables and underground telecommunication cables are in close proximity. This item will be N/A for most EICRs.

- **5.16** Concerns proximity to non-electrical services. Basically, wiring systems should not be installed near other services that produce heat, smoke, or fumes likely to be detrimental to the wiring.

- **5.17** Provides a list of requirements regarding terminations of cables at enclosures. The extent of sampling should be stated in Section D of the report. Inspectors will need to check each of the following:
  - Connections are soundly made and under no undue strain
  - No basic insulation of a conductor visible outside of the enclosure
  - Connections of live conductors are adequately enclosed

- Cables are adequately connected at the point of entry to the enclosure (using glands and bushes, etc.)

Some of these inspection items are covered elsewhere in the schedule when followed correctly, and this repetitive inspection process ensures nothing is missed.

- **5.18** Concerns the condition of accessories, including socket-outlets, switches, and joint boxes. Confirmation is needed that the installation is not damaged or deteriorated in any way that may compromise safety.

- **5.19** Concerns the suitability of accessories for the external influences they are subjected to. Examples of external influences to be considered are listed in inspection item 5.9.

- **5.20** Requires the Inspector to comment on the adequacy of working space or accessibility to equipment. Regulation 132.12 requires sufficient space for the initial installation but also for future replacements. All equipment must be accessible for operation, maintenance, inspection and testing, and repair.

- **5.21** Requires confirmation that there is no single-pole switching of the neutral conductor. Inspections should be made at all relevant points within the installation where CBs, fuses, or switches are installed. Confirmation that this requirement has been met is usually obtained during polarity testing, as required by Regulation 643.6(i).

6.0 Location(s) Containing A Bath Or Shower	
6.1	Additional protection for all low voltage (LV) circuits by RCD not exceeding 30 mA (701.411.3.3)
6.2	Where used as a protective measure, requirements for SELV or PELV met (701.414.4.5)
6.3	Shaver sockets comply with BS EN 61558-2-5 formerly BS 3535 (701.512.3)
6.4	Presence of supplementary bonding conductors, unless not required by BS 7671:2018 (701.415.2)
6.5	Low voltage (e.g. 230 volt) socket-outlets sited at least 3 m from zone 1 (701.512.3)
6.6	Suitability of equipment for external influences for installed location in terms of IP rating (701.512.2)
6.7	Suitability of accessories and controlgear etc. for a particular zone (701.512.3)
6.8	Suitability of current-using equipment for particular position within the location (701.55)
7.0 Other Part 7 Special Installations Or Locations	
7.01	List all other special installation or locations, if any (record seperately the results of particular inspections applied).

Fig 8.11 Extract of inspection schedule Sections 6 and 7

Inspection Items 6.0 to 6.8: Location(s) containing a bath or shower, see Fig 8.11

- **6.1** Concerns additional protection, Inspectors, will need to check for the presence of an RCD not exceeding 30 mA protection for all LV circuits in the bathroom.

- **6.2** Where a SELV or PELV system has been used as a protective measure, Inspectors, will need to confirm that the requirements of Section 414 have been met. Where used, basic protection shall be provided by insulation and/or suitable barriers or enclosures.

- Regulation 414.3 provides a list of suitable sources that may be used for SELV and PELV systems, such as a safety isolating transformer. Inspectors will need to confirm that the source is suitable, e.g., safety isolating transformer to BS EN 61558-2-6 or BS EN 61558-2-8.

- **6.3** Requires confirmation that where shaver sockets are installed, they comply with the British Standard BS EN 61558-2-5 (formerly BS 3535); only this type of shaver socket is permitted in bathrooms. There are other types, such as the BS 4573 shaver socket, and therefore Inspectors will need to remove the shaver for inspection and confirmation of the correct standard. Inspectors should also check the shaver unit is correctly located. BS EN 61558-2-5 units must not be installed in zones 0 or 1. They are only permitted to be installed in zone 2 or outside of the zones; see Fig 8.12 for zone details.

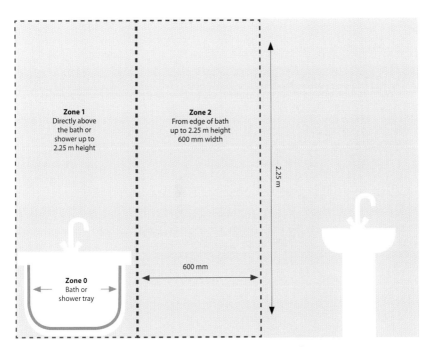

Fig 8.12 Zone dimensions for locations containing a bath or a shower

- **6.4** Concerns additional protection, where the Inspector will be checking for the presence and adequacy of supplementary bonding (where required).

see Fig 8.13 for more detail. With more RCDs being used in recent installations, often, this form of protection can be omitted, where any required main protective bonding has been verified in accordance with BS 7671.

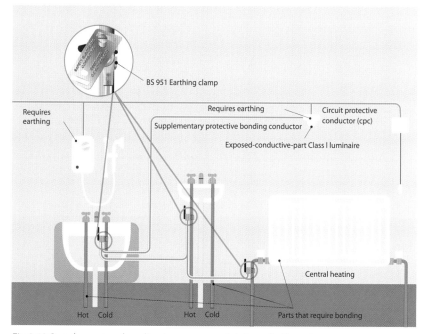

Fig 8.13 Supplementary bonding in a room containing a bath or shower

- **6.5** Concerns the positioning of socket-outlets, except for SELV socket-outlets and shaver supply units, there should be a minimum distance of 3 m horizontally from the boundary of zone 1.

- **6.6** Concerns the suitability of the equipment in terms of IP rating. In simple terms, the IP rating is a rating scale used to gauge the suitability of openings in any enclosure. Different environments require different IP ratings; in this case, the equipment will be exposed to water and humidity and needs to be suitably rated. The inspection shall check the equipment must be appropriate for the zone where it is installed. As follows:

    - Equipment in zone 0 requires a minimum degree of protection of IPX7

    - Equipment in zone 1 and 2 requires a minimum degree of protection of IPX4

- Where equipment is exposed to water jets, protection should be to IPX5

The above degrees of protection do not apply to shaver supply units complying with BS EN 61558-2-5 when installed in zone 2 if direct spray from showers is unlikely.

- **6.7** Requires confirmation that any electrical accessories or control gear is suitable for the zone location.
  - Zone 0: No switchgear or accessories are permitted unless incorporated into fixed current-using equipment suitable for use in that zone. See Regulation 701.512.3 for full requirements.
  - Zone 1: Only switches of SELV circuits (12 V AC or 30 V DC maximum) are permitted (provided the safety source is installed outside of the zones). Only permanently connected equipment suitable for zone 1 (according to manufacturer's instructions) should be installed.
  - Zone 2: Only switches and socket-outlets of SELV circuits are permitted, provided the safety source is installed outside of the zones. Shaver units to BS EN 61558-2-5 are also permitted.

- **6.8** Requires confirmation that current using electrical equipment is suitable for the zone location. The following list of equipment is recognised as suitable for zone 1 if permanently connected declared suitable by the manufacturer:
  - Electric showers
  - Shower pumps
  - whirlpool units
  - Equipment protected by SELV or PELV (25 V AC or 60 V DC maximum) with safety source outside zones
  - Ventilation and extraction equipment
  - Towel rails
  - Water heaters
  - Luminaires

Inspection item 7.0: Other Part 7 special installations or locations

- **7.1** Requires the Inspector to list all other special installations or locations present and record the results separately. BS 7671 has a part dedicated to such locations, Part 7. Not all Part 7s will be relevant, and therefore, it is down to the Inspector to include only the applicable inspections.

8.3 Testing

Where there is a requirement for any testing to be carried out for an EICR, it should be carried out using the procedure outlined in Section 6 of this Guide, using any and all required safe isolation procedures contained within Section 4 of this Guide. Any test results obtained must be recorded on a Schedule of test results, in accordance with Section 6 of this Guide.

8.4 Report Codes and classifications

When carrying out an EICR, in accordance with BS 7671, the observations found are given a classification code. Each classification code denotes that a given observation or part of an inspection schedule has either been inspected, noted as a limitation, or deemed not applicable to the installation.

The EICR Inspection schedule provides a list of items to be inspected. The outcome of each inspection should be marked with one of the following outcomes:

- ✓ Acceptable condition
- **C1** Danger present (Unacceptable condition)
- **C2** Potentially dangerous (Unacceptable condition)
- **C3** Improvement recommended (Acceptable condition)
- **FI** Further investigation (Unacceptable condition)
- **L** Limitation
- **N/A** Not applicable

Additional comments made by the Inspector should be put in Section K of the report for any **C1**, **C2**, **C3**, or **FI** Classification Codes issued. This allows the person carrying out any remedial works, to understand the nature and location of any observations.

8.4.1 **C1** – Danger present, immediate remedial action required (Unacceptable condition)

Classification code **C1** is given to any observations where the Inspector considers that an immediate risk of injury is present. An immediate risk is usually taken as an electric shock or associated with an electrical fire risk. An example of this could be where safety blanks are missing from the front of a consumer unit, allowing access to live parts. BS 7671 requires immediate remedial action for such observations.

8.4.1.1 C1 – Client/Duty holder notification

An Inspector has a duty of care to inform the Client, Duty holder, or person ordering the report of any observations that warrant a C1 code, as a matter of urgency. This can be verbally or in any written or electronic media format and must be able to be evidenced by the Inspector.

Any C1 notification to the Client, duty holder, or person ordering the work can also be backed up in writing by issuing a dangerous situation report (DSR), or similar, see Fig 8.14 NAPIT DSR.

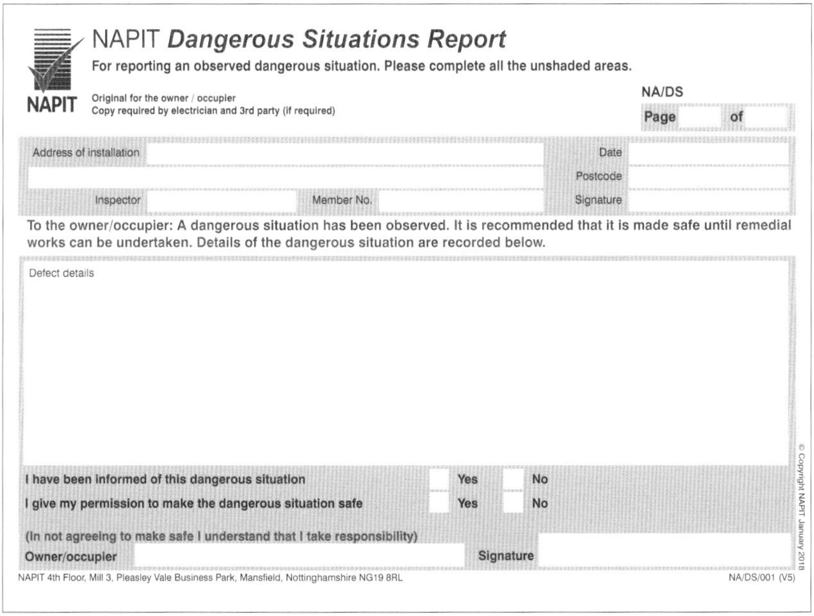

NAPIT **Dangerous Situations Report**

For reporting an observed dangerous situation. Please complete all the unshaded areas.

NAPIT

Original for the owner / occupier
Copy required by electrician and 3rd party (if required)

NA/DS

Page   of

Address of installation		Date	
		Postcode	
Inspector	Member No.	Signature	

To the owner/occupier: A dangerous situation has been observed. It is recommended that it is made safe until remedial works can be undertaken. Details of the dangerous situation are recorded below.

Defect details

I have been informed of this dangerous situation	Yes	No
I give my permission to make the dangerous situation safe	Yes	No

(In not agreeing to make safe I understand that I take responsibility)

Owner/occupier   Signature

NAPIT 4th Floor, Mill 3, Pleasley Vale Business Park, Mansfield, Nottinghamshire NG19 8RL   NA/DS/001 (V5)

© Copyright NAPIT January 2018

Fig 8.14 NAPIT DSR

By informing the Client or duty holder, etc., of the presence of a C1 observation, the Inspector has discharged their legal duty under any HSE requirements, and any further liability rests with the Client or duty holder.

When agreeing on items for inspection, etc., before the EICR commences, it is acceptable for C1 codes to be rectified, during the inspection process, by the Inspector, where permission and guidelines for this have been laid down with the Client or person ordering the work.

Where they have been authorised to do so, an Inspector may isolate for safety, the equipment or circuit in question. Where a circuit has been isolated for safety reasons, it should not be re-energised until it has been satisfactorily repaired.

If the observation is serious enough or the Inspector feels their safety, the safety of their employees or others may be compromised; they may call the inspection process to a halt and continue only when the ⓒ1 observation has been made safe, isolated, or repaired. The Inspector has a duty of care to their self and others to ensure this happens.

Where a rectification process is in place during an EICR, it's good practice to note on the EICR that these works have taken place to give an understanding of the Electrical Installations condition and general wear and tear; which can be used in the future to assess the frequency of next inspection. As in all rectification work, the correct certification must also be issued where relevant.

A ⓒ1 observation will lead to an unacceptable condition; therefore, resulting in an Unsatisfactory outcome on an EICR.

Note:
Where the EICR is being carried out for a Landlord, in accordance with the 'Electrical Safety Standards in the Private Rented Sector (England) Regulations 2020', the Landlord must have any ⓒ1 findings rectified, no later than 28 days from the date the EICR was carried out.

The Inspector may give less than 28 days for ⓒ1 faults, where they feel it is required for the safety of the tenant; these time periods are at the discretion of the Inspector and cannot be influenced by the Landlord or their agent in any way unless it involves the increased security, safety, or wellbeing of the tenant.

8.4.2 ⓒ2 – Potentially dangerous, urgent remedial action required

The classification code ⓒ2 is given to any observations that fall into the category of potentially dangerous. Usually, something else needs to happen before the danger is present, but the observation is considered unsatisfactory for continued use. An example of this may be a badly cracked socket-outlet; during the inspection, no live parts are showing, so there is no risk of electric shock, but with use, the socket could fall apart, exposing live parts, introducing an electric shock hazard.

There is no requirement for the Inspector to inform the Client or Duty holder etc. with details of C2 observations during the inspection. Any requirement to carry out remedial works is still urgent, but that urgency is decided by the Client or Duty holder, etc.

A C2 observation will lead to an unacceptable condition; therefore, resulting in an Unsatisfactory outcome on an EICR.

Note:
Where the EICR is being carried out for a Landlord's Private Rented Sector EICR, the Landlord and must have any C2 findings rectified, no later than 28 days from the date of the EICR.

8.4.3 C3 – Improvement recommended

The classification code C3 Improvement recommended is given where the Inspector feels that the overall safety of the installation will be improved if the recommendation is actioned.

An example of this may be poor labelling of electrical equipment that does not fall into the category of potentially dangerous, but the improvement will enhance safety.

Where safety issues have been highlighted within industry, or a governing body and either or both feel that a C2, and therefore an unacceptable outcome be given to instances, where an installation complied to a previous edition of BS 7671 and, that now may be dangerous to users of electrical installations, or emergency services during the execution of their duties. Examples of this would be:

- Socket outlets, without ≤ 30 mA RCD protection, supplying (or known to supply) equipment outside.
- Cables are not adequately supported against premature collapse in the event of a fire.
- Cables buried in walls at less than 50 mm, without ≤ 30 mA RCD protection.

Reports with no or only ③ observations will lead to a Satisfactory outcome.

8.4.4 ⓕ – Further investigation required without delay

This observation Code is given where further investigation or clarification is required to ascertain the outcome of the observation, but it is likely that it will be either a Code ⓒ① or ⓒ②. The importance rating is that of the ⓒ②, in so much as the inspection can carry on, unless the Inspector feels there is a likelihood of a serious safety breach.

An example of an ⓕ could be that the Inspector has obtained an unsatisfactory test result pointing towards cable insulation damage. The damage could be considerable; for example, a cable has been gnawed by vermin, and there may be a bare copper cable. Clearly, this is unacceptable and presents both a risk of fire (should the cables arc together), or an electric shock hazard (should they be touched).

There may be a more innocent reason for the unsatisfactory test result, such as moisture present in an outside light fitting or a trapped/pinched cable in the back of a socket-outlet. Only further investigation will reveal the extent of the problem and may take considerable time, which is often the case with fault finding. Therefore, this extra work is often carried out separately to the EICR.

An ⓕ observation will lead to an unacceptable condition; therefore, resulting in an Unsatisfactory outcome on an EICR.

Note:
Where the EICR is being carried out for a Landlord, in accordance with the 'Electrical Safety Standards in the Private Rented Sector (England) Regulations 2020', the Landlord must have any ⓕ findings investigated, no later than 28 days from the date the EICR was carried out.

If the outcome of these Further Investigations highlights either a ⓒ① or ⓒ②, the Landlord will have up to 28 days to rectify the fault highlighted by the Further Investigation.

The Inspector may reduce the time period for rectification of a ⓒ① fault; where they feel this is required for the safety of the tenant. Any reduction in the time period of 28 days for the rectification of a ⓒ① fault cannot be influenced by the Landlord or their agent in any way, unless it involves the increased security, safety, or wellbeing of the tenant.

8.4.5 Observations and Coding

As installations and their uses vary considerably, it is very difficult to give a definitive code for a particular observation, for example, what may be a **C2** on one installation, maybe a **C3** on another, depending on any control measures or usage restrictions that are in place.

To help with this part of the EICR process NAPIT have produced a Guide to EICR coding called:

'EICR Codebreakers, A Guide to Coding Observations for Electrical Installation Condition Reports (EICRs)'

This publication gives guidance on where the Coding process can begin, for a given level of installation, allowing Inspectors to apply judgement from this point. Where an Inspector feels a more or less severe Code than the one suggested is relevant, they are free to Code accordingly but must be prepared to take responsibility for this.

Codebreaker contains Approximately 640 Observations and Codes as well as guidance for Inspectors on Non-BS 7671 observations, DNO contact details, SPDs and RCD Selectivity and how to code them.

Codebreaker can be obtained from the following outlets

www.napitdirect.co.uk

Codebreaker is also available in electronic format, using the Vital Source Platform, with redemption codes available from:

www.napitdirect.co.uk

8.4.6 Remaining Observation Codes

When individual items are inspected, if they don't attract a classification code **C1**, **C2**, **C3**, or **FI**, the outcome may be marked with one of the following outcomes:

✅ Acceptable condition

Inspection items with a tick in the inspection schedule outcome box are deemed acceptable for continued use, requiring no other comments from the Inspector.

(N/A) Not applicable

Not all inspection items are relevant; for example, there is a requirement to check surge protection devices (SPD) are functional; however, if the installation does not have SPDs fitted, then N/A should be used.

⚠️ Agreed Limitation

A limitation is a part of the inspection procedure that should have been mutually agreed between the Inspector and the Client, Duty holder, or person ordering the work before the inspection takes place. It denotes where a particular check or test is not carried out but is acceptable as it has been agreed prior to the inspection starting. Agreed and Operational Limitations are covered earlier in this Section.

8.5 Frequency of Inspection and/or Testing

After the initial verification of an electrical installation, Regulation 644.4 gives requirements for how the first inspection frequency should be determined. The wording of this Regulation requires that the person responsible for the design, construction, and verification of the installation takes account of their responsibilities to the person ordering the work when setting the frequency for the first periodic inspection.

This means, if the inspection is a bespoke or commissioned installation, the eventual user or person responsible for its end use should be consulted as to its use, and therefore a requirement for the first initial inspection frequency. Where the installation is a generic design that may then be rented or leased, as would be in the case of residential flats, office, and business units, for example, it is harder to define the initial inspection frequency. Users in these cases, and indeed the actual use of an installation, may not be fully known.

There are also legislative requirements for 'maximum' frequencies of inspection and testing, for the private rented sector, in England, Scotland and Wales. In all of these cases, the government websites for individual countries should be consulted to ensure the correct maximum frequencies and any other requirements are adhered to.

The newest Legislation for the Private rented sector is:

'The Electrical Safety Standards in the Private Rented Sector (England) Regulations 2020'

This new Legislation requires a maximum frequency of inspection and testing of no more than 5 years. As this is a maximum, not a minimum frequency. Where damage or consistent abuse, etc., is witnessed by the Inspector, frequencies of less than 5 years can be recommended, see 3 (2)(b) of the associated new Legislation.

8.5.1 Previous/existing installation information

After the first periodic inspection, the frequency, or the interval for the next periodic inspection, should be calculated in line with Regulation 653.4, which requires the next recommended interval or frequency to be supported by an explanation for the recommendation. This should be an easier process as historical knowledge of the installation, and its use should be available.

When you are asked to provide a supporting explanation for recommending the period to the next inspection, you are being asked to assess the risk for the safety of the installation, or your Client is. Your Client should provide a detailed supporting risk assessment for their recommendation for the next inspection. This is very important; only your Client has a detailed knowledge of their installation, its actual use (not what you saw in the short time you were on-site), and only they can prevent areas of potential damage with control measures, procedures, and maintenance programs.

If they have documented paperwork to suggest that this will happen, going forward, and have historical data to either backup or strengthen their control measures, they are quite within their rights to state when they next have a periodic inspection carried out on their electrical installation.

Note:
The frequency given by the Inspector is only a recommendation; the Client has a right to decrease that frequency if they feel their control measures are robust enough. Likewise, they have an obligation to increase them if their risk assessment requires more frequent inspections.

Guidance on understanding what a Risk Assessment is and how to carry out an effective one can be found in NAPIT's publication, 'Risk Assessment and Management Code of Practice.' Written for all aspects of business and gives guidance for Clients and Inspectors alike. Currently available in electronic format using the Vital Source Platform, with redemption codes available from:

www.napitdirect.co.uk

8.5.2 Client/Duty holders' responsibilities

It is important to understand that the Client, Duty holder, or responsible person for the electrical installation is the only person responsible for the ongoing electrical safety of an installation. Only they are responsible for assessing the safety pertaining to its use, and only they are responsible for any shortcomings in controlling these risks.

Your Client, Duty holder or the responsible person for their installation, can take the advice of a third-party inspector or contractor into account, but they are in no way responsible for any following issues which relate directly to electrical safety or frequencies of inspections. Sole responsibility lies with the Client or responsible person.

8.5.3 Maximum frequencies between inspections and any testing

Frequencies recommended between inspection and any testing should be determined by a risk assessment and discussed with the Client. An important factor here is to agree on what is in place to ensure an electrical installation is safe and how it has been modified or maintained in the past.

The only way to assess an electrical installations likelihood of damage referenced against any control measures, that are either in place or needed can only be achieved with a detailed risk assessment. Detailed risk assessment methods for determining frequencies can be found in NAPIT's EICR Codebreaker publication.

Without a risk assessment, the Inspector will need to use some form of guidance to achieve a frequency that will keep an installation's user safe. A sliding scale of frequencies based on control measures and known factors is given in Table 3.5 of NAPIT's EICR Codebreakers publication, available from the NAPIT Direct website.

www.napitdirect.co.uk

8.6 EICR completion and documentation

Once the EICR is completed, it is only a complete document when all of its constituent parts are included. Along with all of the completed inspection and test schedules, the Inspector will give an overall summary of the installation and also state whether it is Satisfactory or Unsatisfactory.

8.6.1 Overall summary

As an overall summary, the Inspector may mention observations that are not relevant to BS 7671 but may form part of their thought process to assigning a particular frequency for the next inspection or test. These observations can include:

- The state of repair of the installation
- Modifications that may not be of a good quality
- Evidence of maintenance, or the lack of it
- Evidence of environmental damage
- User practices that may damage the installation

8.6.1.1 Satisfactory

Where an EICR is marked as 'Satisfactory,' this is an indication that it is safe for continued use and has no dangerous faults **C1**, potentially dangerous faults **C2** or Further Investigation requirements **FI**.

There may be observations that are coded **C3**, recommends improvement, but these are for the Client or Duty holders' discretion to upgrade and should not impede the overall safety of the installation.

Note:
Although **C3** Coded observations are seen as Satisfactory, the Client or duty holder has a duty of care to the users of the installations they are responsible for. Other Health and Safety Legislation, best practice, or legal constraints may require that **C3** recommendations are given consideration dependent on the installations use.

8.6.1.2 Unsatisfactory

Where an EICR outcome is Unsatisfactory, there should be suitable details provided in Section K to justify why the installation is unsatisfactory in terms of electrical safety.

This may involve the use of additional pages attached to the EICR. Where the Inspector attaches additional information to the report, the page numbers should be clearly referenced.

8.6.2 Completed documentation

A completed EICR should normally consist of at least 5 pages and include the following completed documentation:

- Fig 8.15 **EICR front sheet(s)**
- Fig 8.16 **Inspection Schedule(s)**
- Fig 8.17 **Schedule of Test Result(s)**
- Fig 8.18 **Notes for the person producing the Report**
- Fig 8.19 **Guidance for the recipients**
- Fig 8.20 **Guidance for the Inspector**

Electrical Installation Condition Report

for Domestic and Similar Premises up to 100 A Supply
Requirements for Electrical Installations
BS 7671:2018 (IET Wiring Regulations 18th Edition)

NAPIT

NA/	1	2	3	4	5	6	7	0	0	0	0	0	1
EICR							Page	1	of	5			

A Details of the Installation

Client M Smith

Installation House Dwelling

Address 101 Park Road
Park Lane
Parkford

Address Same as client

Postcode PAK1 2PF

Postcode

B Reason for producing this report This form is to be used only for reporting on the condition of an existing installation.

Rented accommodation, Insurance purposes.

Date(s) on which the inspection and testing were carried out 14/04/2020 to 14/04/2020

C Details of installation which is the subject of this report

Description of premises Domestic ✓ Commercial ☐ Industrial ☐ Other (please specify) N/A

Estimated age of the wiring system 10 years

Evidence of alterations or addition Yes ✓ No ☐ Not apparent ☐ if 'Yes', estimated 3 years

Records of installation available Yes ✓ No ☐ Records held by client

Date of last inspection 14/04/2015 Electrical Installation Certificate No. or previous Inspection Report No. 444444444000001

D

Extent of electrical installation covered by this report:
All circuits from D/B 1

Agreed Limitations and Operational Limitations (Regulations 653.2)
none

Operational limitations including the reasons see page no N/A of N/A Agreed with: N/A

The inspection and testing detailed within this report and accompanying schedule has been carried out in accordance with BS 7671: 2018 amended to 2020

It should be noted that cables concealed within the trunkings and conduits, under floors, in roof spaces and generally within the fabric of the building or underground have not been inspected unless specifically agreed between the client and inspector prior to the inspection. An inspection should be made within an accessible roof space housing other electrical equipment.

E Summary of the condition of the installation

General conditions of the installation (in terms of safety)
Good condition with two recommendations

Overall assessment of the installation in terms of its suitability for continued use **SATISFACTORY** ✓ *UNSATISFACTORY ☐

*An UNSATISFACTORY assessment indicates that dangerous (code C1), or potentially dangerous (code C2). Further investigation (code FI) conditions have been identified

F Recommendations

Where the overall assessment of the suitability of the installation for continued use above is stated as UNSATISFACTORY I/we recommend that any observations classified as 'Danger present' (**code C1**) or 'Potentially dangerous' (**code C2**) are acted upon as a matter of urgency. Investigation without delay is recommended for observations identified as 'Further Investigation required' (**code FI**). Observations classified as 'Improvement recommended' (**code C3**) should be given due consideration. Subject to the necessary remedial action being taken, I/we recommend that the installation is further inspected and tested by 14/04/2025 date)

G Declaration

I/we being the person(s) responsible for the inspection and the testing of the electrical installation (as indicated by my/our signatures below), particulars of which are described above, having exercised reasonable skill and care when carrying out the inspection and testing hereby declare that the information in this report, including the observations and the attached schedules, provides an accurate assessment of the condition of the electrical installation taking into account the stated extent and limitations in section D of this report.

Company Techsafe

Membership No. 1234567

Address 77 Street Top road

Postcode TR1 1TR

	Inspected and tested by	Authorised for issue by
Name:	Mr Toptech	Mr Toptech
Signature:	Top Tech	Top Tech
Position:	Electrician	Electrician
Date:	14/04/2020	14/04/2020

H Schedule(s)

1 schedule(s) of inspection and 1 schedule(s) of test results are attached.

The attached schedule(s) are part of this document and this report is valid only when they are attached to it.

Created by NAPIT © Copyright NAPIT 2018

NAPIT Administration Centre, 4th Floor, Mill 3, Pleasley Vale Business Park, Mansfield, Nottinghamshire NG19 8RL

NA/EICR/001

Fig 8.15 EICR Front Sheet(s)

Electrical Installation Condition Report

for Domestic and Similar Premises up to 100 A Supply
Requirements for Electrical Installations
BS 7671:2018 (IET Wiring Regulations 18th Edition)

NAPIT

NA/ | 1 | 2 | 3 | 4 | 5 | 6 | 7 | 0 | 0 | 0 | 0 | 1

EICR | Page 2 of 5

I Supply characteristics and earthing arrangements

Earthing Arrangements — TN-S ☐ TN-C-S ✓ TT ☐ Other ☐ Please specify N/A

Number & Type of live conductors — AC ✓ DC ☐ No. of phases 1 No. of wires 2

Nature of Supply Parameters (Note: (1) by enquiry, (2) by enquiry or by measurement)

Nominal voltage, U/U₀ (1) 230 v | Nominal frequency, f (1) 50 Hz | Confirmation of polarity ✓

Prospective fault current, I_pf (2) 0.7 kA | External loop impedance, Z_e (2) 0.35 Ω | Or Z_db Source of Circuit N/A

Supply Protective Device BS (EN) 1361 | Type 2 | Rated Current 100 A

Other Sources of Supply (as detailed on attached schedule) N/A

J Particulars of installation referred to in this report

Details of installation Earth Electrode (where applicable) Type (e.g. rod(s), tape etc) N/A | **Means of Earthing**

Location N/A | Electrode resistance to earth N/A Ω | Distributors facility ✓ Installation Earth Electrode ☐

Main Protective Conductors	Material	csa	(✓) or Value		Maximum Demand (load) 80 Amps ✓ KVA ☐

Earthing Conductor — Copper — 16 — ✓ N/A Ω | (connection / continuity) (✓) or Value | | (✓) or Value

Protective Bonding Conductor (to extraneous-conductive-parts) — Copper — 10 — ✓ | Water installation ✓ N/A Ω | To structural steel ☐ Ω

Main Supply Conductor — Copper — 25 | Gas installation pipes ✓ N/A Ω | To lightning protection ☐ Ω

Main Switch Location DB 1 kitchen | Oil installation pipes ☐ Ω | Other ☐ Ω

Fuse/device rating or setting Switch A Voltage rating 230 V | BS(EN) 60947-3 | No. of Poles 2 | Current Rating 100 A

If RCD main switch: Rated residual operating current I Δn N/A mA | Rated time delay N/A ms | Measured operating trip time N/A ms

K Observations

Referring to the attached schedule of inspection and test results, and subject to the limitations at Section D.

Explanation of codes

- (C1) Danger present. Risk of injury. Immediate remedial action required.
- (C2) Potentially dangerous. Urgent remedial action required.
- (C3) Improvement recommended.
- (FI) Further investigation required without delay

☐ No remedial work required

✓ The following observations are made

Item No.	Observations	Code
1	Consumer Unit has restricted access	(C3)
2	Sockets mounted too low	(C3)

One of the above codes, as appropriate, has been allocated to each of the observations made above and/or any attached observation sheets to indicate to the person(s) responsible for the installation the degree of urgency for remedial action.

Danger present. Risk of Injury. Immediate remedial action required.	
Potentially dangerous. Urgent remedial action required.	
Improvement recommended.	1, 2.
Further Investigation required without delay	

NA/EICR/001

Fig 8.15 EICR Front Sheet(s) continuation

Electrical Installation Condition Report Inspection Schedule

for Domestic and Similar Premises up to 100 A Supply
Requirements for Electrical Installations - BS 7671:2018 (IET Wiring Regulations 18th Edition) All items inspections to confirm as appropriate, compliance with the relevant clauses in BS 7671:2018

NAPIT

NA/	1	2	3	4	5	6	7	0	0	0	0	0	1
EICR								Page	3	of	5		

Outcomes

Acceptable condition: ✓	Unacceptable condition: State C1 or C2	Improvement recommended: C3	Further Investigation: FI	Not Verified: N/V	Limitation: ⚠	Not Applicable: N/A

In the outcome column use the codes above. Provide additional comment where appropriate. C1/C2/C3 and FI coded items to be recorded in section K of the condition report.

Item No.	Description	Outcome
1.0 External Condition Of Intake Equipment (Visual Inspection Only) Where inadequacies are encountered, it is recommended that the person ordering the report informs the appropriate authority		
1.1	Service cable	✓
1.2	Service head	✓
1.3	Earthing arrangement	✓
1.4	Meter tails	✓
1.5	Metering equipment	✓
1.6	Isolator (where present)	✓
2.0	Presence Of Adequate Arrangements For Other Sources Such As Microgenerators (551.6; 551.7)	N/A
3.0 Earthing / Bonding Arrangements (411.3; Chap 54)		
3.1	Presence and condition of distributor's earthing arrangement (542.1.2.1; 542.1.2.2)	✓
3.2	Presence and condition of earth electrode connection where applicable (542.1.2.3)	N/A
3.3	Provision of earthing/bonding labels at all appropriate locations (514.13.1)	✓
3.4	Confirmation of earthing conductor size (542.3; 543.1.1)	✓
3.5	Accessibility and condition of earthing conductor at MET arrangement (543.3.2)	✓
3.6	Confirmation of main protective bonding conductor sizes (544.1)	✓
3.7	Condition and accessibility of main protective bonding conductor/connections (543.3.2; 544.1.2)	✓
3.8	Accessibility and condition of other protective bonding connections (543.3.1; 543.3.2)	N/A
4.0 Consumer Unit(s) / Distribution Board(s)		
4.1	Adequacy of working space/accessibility to consumer unit/distribution board (132.12; 513.1)	C3
4.2	Security of fixing (134.1.1)	✓
4.3	Condition of enclosure(s) in terms of IP rating etc (416.2)	✓
4.4	Condition of enclosure(s) in terms of fire rating etc (421.1.201; 526.5)	✓
4.5	Enclosure not damaged/deteriorated so as to impair safety (651.2)	✓
4.6	Presence of main linked switch (as required by 462.1.201)	✓
4.7	Operation of main switches (functional check) (643.10)	✓
4.8	Manual operation of circuit-breakers and RCD(s) to prove disconnection (643.10)	✓
4.9	Correct identification of circuit details and protective devices (514.8.1; 514.9.1)	✓
4.10	Presence of RCD six-monthly test notice at or near consumer unit/distribution board (514.12.2)	✓
4.11	Presence of non-standard (mixed) cable colour warning notice at or near consumer unit/distribution board (514.14)	✓
4.12	Presence of alternative supply warning notice at or near consumer unit/distribution board (514.15)	N/A
4.13	Presence of other required labelling (please specify) (Section 514)	N/A
4.14	Compatibility of protective devices, bases and other components; correct type and rating (No signs of unacceptable thermal damage, arcing or overheating) (411.3.2; 411 4; 411 5; 411 6; section 432.433)	✓
4.15	Single-pole switching or protective devices in line conductor only (132.14.1; 530.3.3)	✓
4.16	Protection against mechanical damage where cables enter consumer unit/distribution board (132.14.1; 522.8.1; 522.8.5; 522.8.11)	✓
4.17	Protection against electromagnetic effects where cables enter consumer unit/distribution board/enclosures (521.5.1)	✓
4.18	RCD(s) provided for fault protection - includes RCBOs (411.4.204; 411.5.2; 531.2)	✓
4.19	RCD(s) provided for additional protection/requirements - includes RCBOs (411.3.3; 415.1)	✓
4.20	Confirmation of indication that SPD is functional (651.4)	N/A
4.21	Confirmation that ALL conductor connections, including connections to busbars, are correctly located in terminals and are tight and secure (526.1)	✓
4.22	Adequate arrangements where a generating set operates as a switched alternative to the public supply (551.6)	N/A
4.23	Adequate arrangements where a generating set operates in parallel with the public supply (551.7)	N/A
5.0 Final Circuits		
5.1	Identification of conductors (514.3.1)	✓
5.2	Cables correctly supported throughout their run (521.10.202; 522.8.5)	✓
5.3	Condition of insulation of live parts (416.1)	✓

Created by NAPIT © Copyright NAPIT 2018
NAPIT Administration Centre, 4th Floor, Mill 3, Pleasley Vale Business Park, Mansfield, Nottinghamshire NG19 8RL

NA/EICR/001

Fig 8.16 EICR Inspection schedule(s)

Electrical Installation Condition Report Inspection Schedule

for Domestic and Similar Premises up to 100 A Supply
Requirements for Electrical Installations - BS 7671:2018 (IET Wiring Regulations 18th Edition) All items inspections to confirm as appropriate, compliance with the relevant clauses in BS 7671:2018

| NA/ | 1 | 2 | 3 | 4 | 5 | 6 | 7 | 0 | 0 | 0 | 0 | 0 | 1 |
| EICR | | | | | | | | | Page | 4 | of | 5 |

5.4	Non-sheathed cables protected by enclosure in conduit, ducting or trunking. Integrity of containment (521.10.1)	(N/A)
5.4.1	To include the integrity of conduit and trunking systems (metallic and plastic)	(N/A)
5.5	Adequacy of cables for current-carrying capacity with regard for the type and nature of installation (Section 523)	✓
5.6	Coordination between conductors and overload protective devices (433.1; 533.2.1)	✓
5.7	Adequacy of protective devices: type and rated current for fault protection (411.3)	✓
5.8	Presence and adequacy of circuit protective conductors (433.3.1; Section 543)	✓
5.9	Wiring system(s) appropriate for the type and nature of the installation and external influences (Section 522)	✓
5.10	Concealed cables installed in prescribed zones (see Section D. Extent and limitations) (522.6.202)	✓
5.11	Cables concealed under floors, above ceilings or in walls/partitions, adequately protected against damage (see Section D. Extent and limitations) (522.6.204)	(N/A)
5.12	**Provision of additional requirements for protection by RCD not exceeding 30 mA**	
5.12.1	For all socket-outlets of rating 32 A or less, unless an exception is permitted (411.3.3)	✓
5.12.2	For the supply of mobile equipment not exceeding 32 A rating for use outdoors (411.3.3)	✓
5.12.3	For cables concealed in walls at a depth of less than 50 mm (522.6.202; 522.6.203)	✓
5.12.4	For cables concealed in walls/partitions containing metal parts regardless of depth (522.6.203)	(N/A)
5.12.5	For circuits supplying luminaires within domestic (household) premises (411.3.4)	✓
5.13	Provision of fire barriers, sealing arrangements and protection against thermal effects (Section 527)	✓
5.14	Band II cables segregated/separated from Band I cables (528.1)	(N/A)
5.15	Cables segregated/separated from communications cabling (528.2)	(N/A)
5.16	Cables segregated/separated from non-electrical services (528.3)	✓
5.17	**Termination of cables at enclosures - indicate extent of sampling in Section D of the report (Section 526)**	
5.17.1	Connections soundly made and under no undue strain (526.6)	✓
5.17.2	No basic insulation of a conductor visible outside enclosure (526.8)	✓
5.17.3	Connections of live conductors adequately enclosed (526.5)	✓
5.17.4	Adequately connected at point of entry to enclosure (glands, bushes etc.) (522.8.5)	✓
5.18	Condition of accessories including socket-outlets, switches and joint boxes (651.2(v))	(LIM)
5.19	Suitability of accessories for external influences (512.2)	✓
5.20	Adequacy of working space/accessibility to equipment (132.12; 513.1)	✓
5.21	Single-pole switching or protective devices in line conductors only (132.14.1, 530.3.3)	✓
6.0 Location(s) Containing A Bath Or Shower		
6.1	Additional protection for all low voltage (LV) circuits by RCD not exceeding 30 mA (701.411.3.3)	(N/A)
6.2	Where used as a protective measure, requirements for SELV or PELV met (701.414.4.5)	(N/A)
6.3	Shaver sockets comply with BS EN 61558-2-5 formerly BS 3535 (701.512.3)	✓
6.4	Presence of supplementary bonding conductors, unless not required by BS 7671:2018 (701.415.2)	(N/A)
6.5	Low voltage (e.g. 230 volt) socket-outlets sited at least 3 m from zone 1 (701.512.3)	(N/A)
6.6	Suitability of equipment for external influences for installed location in terms of IP rating (701.512.2)	✓
6.7	Suitability of accessories and controlgear etc. for a particular zone (701.512.3)	✓
6.8	Suitability of current-using equipment for particular position within the location (701.55)	✓
7.0 Other Part 7 Special Installations Or Locations		
7.1	List all other special installation or locations, if any (record separately the results of particular inspections applied). See sheet:	

8.0 Schedule of Test   Results to be recorded on Schedule of Test Result

8.1	External earth loop impedance, Ze	✓	8.9	Insulation Resistance between Live Conductors	✓
8.2	Installation earth electrode	(N/A)	8.10	Insulation Resistance between Live Conductors & Earth	✓
8.3	Prospective fault current, Ipf	✓	8.11	Polarity (prior to energisation)	✓
8.4	Continuity of Earth Conductors	✓	8.12	Polarity (after energisation) including phase sequence	✓
8.5	Continuity of Circuit Protective Conductors	✓	8.13	Earth Fault Loop Impedance	✓
8.6	Continuity of Ring Final Circuit	✓	8.14	RCDs/RCBOs including selectivity	✓
8.7	Continuity of Protective Bonding Conductors	✓	8.15	Functional testing of RCD devices	✓
8.8	Volt drop verified	(N/A)	8.16	Functional testing of AFDD(s) devices	(N/A)

Inspector's Name:	Mr Toptech	Signature:	*Top Tech*
Date:	14/04/2020		

NA/EICR/001

Fig 8.16 EICR Inspection schedule(s) continuation

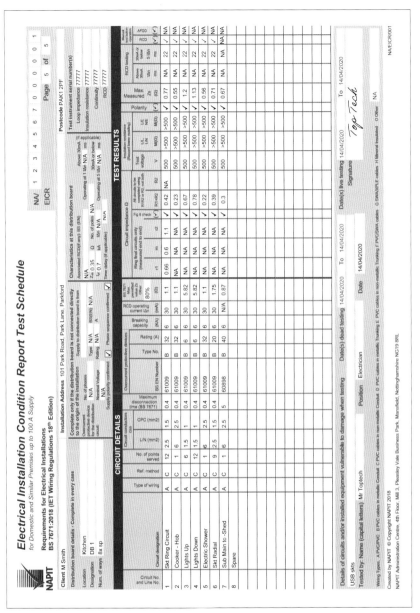

Fig 8.17 EICR Schedule of test result(s)

NAPIT *Electrical Installation Condition Report*
For Domestic and Similar Premises with up to 100 A Supply

Notes for the person producing the Report:

1. This Report should only be used for reporting on the condition of an existing electrical installation, and not for the replacement of a consume unit/distribution board. An installation which was designed to an earlier edition of the Regulations and which does not fully comply with the current edition is not necessarily unsafe for continued use, or requires upgrading. Only damage, deterioration, defects, dangerous conditions and non-compliance with the requirements of the Regulations, which may give rise to danger, should be recorded.

2. The Report, normally comprising at least six pages, should include schedules of both the inspection and the test results. Additional pages may be necessary for other than a simple installation and for the 'Guidance for recipients'. The number of each page should be indicated, together with the total number of pages involved.

3. The reason for producing this Report, such as change of occupancy or landlord's periodic maintenance, should be identified in Section B.

4. Those elements of the installation that are covered by the Report and those that are not should be identified in Section D (Extent and limitations). These aspects should have been agreed with the person ordering the report and other interested parties before the inspection and testing commenced. Any operational limitations, such as inability to gain access to parts of the installation or an item of equipment, should also be recorded in Section D.

5. The maximum prospective value of fault current (I^{pf}) recorded should be the greater of either the prospective value of short-circuit current or the prospective value of earth fault current.

6. Where an installation has an alternative source of supply a further schedule of supply characteristics and earthing arrangements based upon Section I of this Report should be provided.

7. A summary of the condition of the installation in terms of safety should be clearly stated in Section E. Observations, if any, should be categorised in Section K using the coding C1 to C3 as appropriate. Any observation given a code C1 or C2 classification should result in the overall condition of the installation being reported as unsatisfactory.

8. Wherever practicable, **items classified as 'Danger present' (C1) should be made safe on discovery.**

9. Where this is not possible the owner or user should be given written notification as a matter of urgency.

10. Where an observation requires further investigation (FI) because the inspection has revealed an apparent deficiency which could not, owing to the extent or limitations of the inspection, be fully identified and further investigation may reveal a code C1 or C2 item, this should be recorded within Section K, given the code FI and marked as unsatisfactory in Section E.

11. If the space available for observations in Section K is insufficient, additional pages should be provided as necessary.

12. The date by which the next Electrical Installation Condition Report is recommended should be given in Section F. The interval between inspections should take into account the type and usage of the installation and its overall condition.

Fig 8.18 Notes for the person producing the Report

Electrical Installation Condition Report

Requirements for Electrical Installations - BS7671:2018
NAPIT (IET Wiring Regulations 18th Edition)

Information for recipients:

This Report is an important and valuable document which should be retained for future reference.

The purpose of this report is to confirm, so far as reasonably practicable, whether or not the electrical installation is in a satisfactory condition for continued service (see Section E). The report should identify any damage, deterioration, defects and/or conditions which may give rise to danger (see Section K).

The person ordering the report should have received the original report and the inspector should have retained a duplicate.

The original Report should be retained in a safe place and be made available to any person inspecting or undertaking work on the electrical installation in the future. If the property is vacated, this report will provide the new owner / occupier with details of the condition of the electrical installation at the time the report was issued.

Where the installation incorporates residual current devices (RCDs) there should be a notice at or near the devices stating that they should be tested every 6 months. For safety reasons it is important that these instructions are followed.

Section D (Extent and Limitations) should identify fully the extent of the installation covered by this report and any limitations on the inspection and testing. The Inspector should have agreed these aspects with the person ordering the report and with other interested parties (licencing authority, insurance company, mortgage provider and the like) before the inspection was carried out.

Some operational limitations such as inability to gain access to parts of the installation or an item of equipment may have been encountered during the inspection. The inspector should have noted these in Section D.

For items classified in Section K as C1 ("Danger Present"), the safety of those using the installation is at risk, and it is recommended that a skilled person or persons competent in electrical installation work undertakes the necessary remedial work immediately.

For items classified in Section K as C2 ("Potentially Dangerous"), the safety of those using the installation may be at risk and it is recommended that a skilled person or persons competent in electrical installation work undertakes the necessary remedial work as a matter of urgency.

Where it has been stated in Section K that an observation requires further investigation code FI the inspection has revealed an apparent deficiency which may result on a code C1 or C2 could not, due to the extent or limitations of this inspection, be fully identified. Such observations should be investigated as soon as possible. A further examination of the installation will be necessary, to determine the nature and extent of the apparent deficiency (see Section F).

For safety reasons, the electrical installation should be re-inspected at appropriate intervals by a skilled person or persons competent in such work. The recommended date by which the next inspection is due is stated in Section F of the report under 'Recommendations' and on label at or near to the consumer unit/distribution board.

Fig 8.19 Guidance for the recipient

NAPIT *Electrical Installation Condition Report*

For Domestic and Similar Premises with up to 100 A Supply

GUIDANCE FOR THE INSPECTOR

1 Section 1.0. Where inadequacies in the intake equipment are encountered the inspector should advise the person ordering the work to inform the appropriate authority.

2 Older installations designed prior to BS 7671:2018 may not have been provided with RCDs for additional protection. The absence of such protection should as a minimum be given a code C3 classification (item 5.12).

3 The schedule is not exhaustive.

4 Numbers in brackets are regulation references to specified requirements.

Fig 8.20 Guidance for the Inspector

Earlier sections of this guide have explained the requirements for the main parts of the EICR documentation. The following three parts are often overlooked but are very important and need to be understood by both the Inspector and the recipient of the EICR.

8.6.2.1 Notes for the person producing the report

This part of the EICR lays down the minimum requirements that the Inspector is required to carry out or should pay particular attention to and gives guidance on how to approach their findings.

8.6.2.2 Guidance for recipients

As its name suggests, this part of the EICR gives information to the recipient that can help them to understand the different Sections of the EICR. By giving this information to the recipient, you are helping them to understand the thought process behind the EICR and some of the findings and recommendations contained within it.

8.6.2.3 Guidance for the Inspector

This is often overlooked and contains key guidance for the Inspector. A particular point made in this guidance is that where older installations do not have ≤ 30 mA RCDs for additional protection, it should be recommended that a minimum **C3** is recorded, specifically in Section 5.12 of the EICR inspection Schedule for Domestic and similar premises up to 100 A supply. The same applies for all other installations with supplies ≥ 100 A and is covered in the bullet point list, under Final Circuits – Provision of additional protection by RCD not exceeding 30 mA.

8.7 Remedial actions and documentation

Any remedial actions, which have been highlighted by an EICR, are the sole responsibility of the Client, Duty holder, or person ordering the work. There is no HSE or legal requirement placed on the Inspector, other than to inform the Client/Duty holder, etc., that a **C1** infringement has been identified, which is covered earlier in this Section.

After the Client/Duty Holder, etc., has received the EICR and requirements for remedial action, Further investigation, or recommended improvements, they are responsible for any timescales that these upgrades are carried out within. There are no BS 7671 requirements for timescales, as these can only be governed by the Client, as they alone have control of the electrical installation.

Note:

'The Electrical Safety Standards in the Private Rented Sector (England) Regulations 2020' gives clear and definitive timescales for the rectification of remedial findings in EICRs.

Although covered briefly in this guide, it is recommended that NAPIT's publication covering this topic in greater detail is consulted to fully understand any Legislative requirements. Written to comply with BS 7671, NAPIT's 'Landlords and Electrical Inspectors Guidance for the Private Rented Sector (PRS)' is available from the following outlets:

www.napitdirect.co.uk

'Landlords and Electrical Inspectors Guidance for the Private Rented Sector (PRS)' is also available in electronic format, using the Vital Source Platform, with redemption codes available from:

www.napitdirect.co.uk

8.7.1 Remedial documentation

Whenever an EICR is classified as unsatisfactory, through either a **C1**, **C2**, or **FI** observation, and subsequent Code is only a requirement to implement changes that are highlighted by the unsatisfactory Code.

There is no requirement to initiate a new EICR after remedial action and works have taken place.

In accordance with Section F of the EICR, there is only a requirement to carry out remedial work and certification requiring either a MEIWC or an EIC. Where remedial works have been carried out and certified with a MEIWC or an EIC, all that is required is for this documentation to be attached to the original EICR, which then fulfills its status as satisfactory, in accordance with Section F.

Examples of MEIWCs and EICs can be found in Appendix 1 of this guide.

Appendix 1
NAPIT Certificates and Reports

NAPIT
Electrical Installation
Certificate (Single Signature)

For Domestic and Similar Premises with up to 100 A Supply

**Requirements for Electrical Installations – BS 7671:2018
[IET Wiring Regulations 18th Edition]**

NA/EIC/S001 (V1)

NAPIT Administration Centre
4th Floor, Mill 3
Pleasley Vale Business Park
Mansfield
Nottinghamshire
NG19 8RL

www.napit.org.uk   0345 543 0330   info@napit.org.uk

NAPIT *Electrical Installation Certificate* *(Single Signature)*
Notes for the person producing the Certificate:

This Certificate is an important and valuable document which should be retained for future reference.

The Electrical Installation Certificate is to be used only for the initial certification of a new installation or for an addition or alteration to an existing installation where new circuits have been introduced, or the replacement of a consumer unit/distribution board.

1 It is not to be used for a Periodic Inspection, for which an Electrical Installation Condition Report form should be used. For an addition or alteration which does not extend to the introduction of new circuits, a Minor Electrical Installation Works Certificate may be used. The 'original' Certificate is to be issued to the person ordering the work(Regulation 644.4). A duplicate should be retained by the contractor.

2 This Certificate is only valid if accompanied by the Schedule of Inspections and the Schedule(s) of Test Results.

3 The signatures appended are those of the persons authorised by the companies executing the work of design, construction, inspection and testing respectively. A signatory authorised to certify more than one category of work should sign in each of the appropriate places.

4 The time interval recommended before the first periodic inspection must be inserted.

The proposed date for the next inspection should take into consideration the frequency and quality of maintenance that the installation can reasonably be expected to receive during its intended life, and the period should be agreed between the designer, installer and other relevant parties.

5 The page numbers for each of the Schedule of Inspections and the Schedule(s) of Test Results should be indicated, together with the total number of sheets involved.

6 The maximum prospective value of fault current (I_{pf}) recorded should be the greater of either the prospective value of short-circuit current or the prospective value of earth fault current.

Electrical Certificate Installation/Modification

**Requirements for Electrical Installations - BS 7671:2018
(IET Wiring Regulations 18th Edition)**

Information for recipients:

This safety Certificate has been issued to confirm that the electrical installation work to which it relates has been designed, constructed, inspected and tested in accordance with BS 7671 (the IET Wiring Regulations).

You should have received an original Certificate and the contractor should have retained a duplicate.

If you were the person ordering this work, but not the owner of the installation, you should pass this Certificate, or a copy of it, immediately to the owner.

The original Certificate is to be retained in a safe place and be shown to any person inspecting or undertaking work on the electrical installation in the future.

If you later vacate the property, this Certificate will demonstrate to the new owner that the electrical installation complied with the requirements of BS 7671 at the time the Certificate was issued.

The Construction (Design and Management) Regulations require that, for a project covered by those regulations, a copy of this Certificate, together with schedules, is included in the project health and safety document.

For safety reasons, the electrical installation will need to be re-inspected at appropriate intervals by a skilled person or persons, competent in such work. The maximum time interval recommended before the next inspection is stated on Page 2 under "NEXT INSPECTION".

This Certificate is intended to be issued only for a new electrical installation or for new work associated with an addition or alteration to an existing installation. It should not have been issued for the inspection and testing of an existing electrical installation. An "Electrical Installation Condition Report" should be issued for such an inspection.

This Certificate is only valid if accompanied by the schedule of inspections and the schedule(s) of test results.

Electrical Certificate *Installation/Modification*

for Domestic and Similar Premises up to 100 A Supply

Requirements for Electrical Installations
BS 7671:2018 (IET Wiring Regulations 18th Edition)

NAPIT

1 Details of the Installation

Client	M Smith	Installation	House Dwelling
Address	101 Park Road, Park Lane, Parkford	Address	Same as client
Postcod	PAK1 2PF	Postcode	

2 Description, extent and limitations of the installation (note 5)

Installation is New ☑ Addition ☐ Alteration ☐ Records Available Yes ☐ No ☑ Date of original installation 14/04/2020

Description of installation
House Dwelling and Shed

Extent of installation covered by this certificate
Consumer Unit replacement

Details of departures from BS 7671 (regulations 120.3, 133.1.3 and 133.5)

Details of permitted exception. (regulation 411.3.3) where applicable a suitable risk assessment(s) must be attached to this certificate
None

Risk assessment attached (Non Dwelling ONLY)

3 Declaration For design, construction, inspection and testing (for sole person responsibility)

I being the person responsible for design, construction, inspection and the nature of the electrical installation (as indicated by my signature below), particulars of which are described in Section 2, having exercised reasonable skill and care when carrying out the design, construction, inspection and test hereby CERTIFY that the design, construction, inspection and test for which I have been responsible is to the best of my knowledge and belief in accordance with BS 7671:2018, amended to The extent of liability of the signatory or the signatories is limited to work described in Section 2 as subject of this certificate.

For the DESIGN / CONSTRUCTION / INSPECTION & TEST of the installation:

Company	Techsafe	Signature	*Top Tech*
Inspector Name	Mr Toptech	Position	Electrician
Address	77 Street, Top road	Date	14/04/2020
Postcode	TR1 1TR	Member No.	

Next inspection I the designer recommend that this installation is further inspected after an interval of not more than **5** years

4 Supply characteristics and earthing arrangements

Earthing Arrangements TN-S ☐ TN-C-S ☑ TT ☐ Other ☐ Please specify N/A

Number & Type of live conductors AC ☑ DC ☐ No. of phases 1 No. of wires 2

Nature of Supply Parameters (Note: (1) by enquiry, (2) by enquiry or by measurement)

Nominal voltage, U/U₀ (1) 230 v   Nominal frequency, f (1) 50 Hz   Confirmation of polarity ☑

Prospective fault current, I_pf (2) 0.7 kA   External loop impedance, Z_e (2) 0.35 Ω   Or Z_db Source of Circuit N/A

Supply Protective Device BS (EN) 1361 Type 2 Rated Current 100 A

Other Sources of Supply (as detailed on attached schedule) N/A

5 Particulars of installation referred to in this certificate

Means of Earthing Distributors facility ☑ Installation Earth Electrode ☐

Details of installation Earth Electrode (where applicable) Type (e.g. rod(s), tape etc) N/A

Location N/A Electrode resistance to earth N/A

Main Protective Conductors	Material	csa	(✓) or Value			
Earthing Conductor	Copper	16	☑		Maximum Demand (load) 80	Amps ☑ KVA ☐
Protective Bonding Conductor (to extraneous-conductive-parts)	Copper	10	☑	Ω (connection / continuity) (✓) or Value		(✓) or Value
Main Supply Conductor	Copper	25		Water installation ☑ Ω To structural steel Ω	Gas installation pipes ☑ Ω To lightning protection Ω	Oil installation pipes ☐ Ω Other ☐ Ω

Main Switch Location DB 1 kitchen

Fuse/device rating or setting Switch   A Voltage rating 230 V   BS(EN) 60947-3 No. of Poles 2 Current Rating 100 A

If RCD main switch: Rated residual operating current I Δn N/A mA   Rated time delay N/A ms   Measured operating trip time N/A ms

Comments on existing installation (in case of addition or alteration see section 644.1.2) use continuation sheet if needed
none

(For additions or alterations) cables concealed within trunking and conduits, or cables or conduits concealed under floors, in roof spaces and generally within the fabric of the building or underground may not have been inspected.

Created by NAPIT © Copyright NAPIT 2018
NAPIT Administration Centre, 4th Floor, Mill 3, Pleasley Vale Business Park, Mansfield, Nottinghamshire NG19 8RL
NA/EIC/001

Electrical Certificate *Installation/Modification* **Inspection Schedule**

for Domestic and Similar Premises up to 100 A Supply
Requirements for Electrical Installations - BS 7671:2018 (IET Wiring Regulations 18th Edition) All items inspections to confirm as appropriate, compliance with the relevant clauses in BS 7671:2018

Outcomes

Indicates an inspection has been carried out and the result is satisfactory		Indicates the inspection is not applicable to a particular item	

Item No.	Description	Outcome

1.0 External Condition Of Intake Equipment (Visual Inspection Only) Where inadequacies are encountered, it is recommended that the person ordering the report informs the appropriate authority

1.1	Service cable	✓
1.2	Service head	✓
1.3	Earthing arrangement	✓
1.4	Meter tails	✓
1.5	Metering equipment	✓
1.6	Isolator (where present)	✓

2.0 Parallel Or Switched Alternative Sources Of Supply

| 2.1 | Adequate arrangements where a generating set operates as a switched alternative to the public supply (551.6) | N/A |
| 2.2 | Adequate arrangements where a generating set operates in parallel with the public supply (551.7) | N/A |

3.0 Automatic Disconnection Of Supply, Presence And Adequacy Of Earthing And Protective Bonding Arrangements

3.1	Distributor's earthing arrangement (542.1.2.1; 542.1.2.2)	✓
3.2	Installation earth electrode (where applicable) (542.1.2.3)	N/A
3.3	Earthing conductor and connections, including accessibility (542.3; 543.3.2)	✓
3.4	Main protective bonding conductors and connections, including accessibility (411.3.1.2; 543.3.2; Section 544.1)	✓
3.5	Provision of safety electrical earthing/bonding labels at all appropriate locations (514.13)	✓
3.6	RCD(s) provided for fault protection (411.4.204; 411.5.3)	✓

4.0 Basic Protection, Presence And Adequacy Of Measures To Provide Basic Protection (Prevention Of Contact With Live Parts) Within The Installation

| 4.1 | Insulation of live parts e.g. conductors completely covered with durable insulating material (416.1) | ✓ |
| 4.2 | Barriers or enclosures e.g. correct IP rating (416.2) | ✓ |

5.0 Additional Protection, Presence And Effectiveness Of Additional Protection Methods

| 5.1 | RCD(s) not exceeding 30 mA operating current (415.1; Part 7), see item 8.14 of this schedule | ✓ |
| 5.2 | Supplementary bonding (415.2; Part 7) | N/A |

6.0 Other Methods Of Protection, Presence And Effectiveness Of Methods Which Give Both Basic And Fault Protection

6.1	SELV system, including the source and associated circuits (Section 414)	N/A
6.2	PELV system, including the source and associated circuits (Section 414)	N/A
6.3	Double or reinforced insulation i.e. Class II or equivalent equipment and associated circuits (Section 412)	✓
6.4	Electrical separation for one item of equipment e.g. shaver supply unit (Section 413)	✓

7.0 Consumer Unit(s) / Distribution Board(s)

7.1	Adequacy of access and working space for items of electrical equipment including switchgear (132.12)	✓
7.2	Components are suitable according to assembly manufacturer's instructions or literature (536.4.203)	✓
7.3	Presence of linked main switch(es) (462.1.201)	✓
7.4	Isolators, for every circuit or group of circuits and all items of equipment (462.2)	✓
7.5	Suitability of enclosure(s) for IP and fire ratings (416.2; 421.1.6; 421.1.201; 526.5)	✓
7.6	Protection against mechanical damage where cables enter equipment (522.8.1; 522.8.5; 522.8.11)	✓
7.7	Confirmation that ALL conductor connections are correctly located in terminals and are tight and secure (526.1)	✓
7.8	Avoidance of heating effects where cables enter ferromagnetic enclosures e.g. steel (521.5)	✓
7.9	Selection of correct type and ratings of circuit protective devices for overcurrent and fault protection (411.3.2; 411.4, 411.5, 411.6; Sections 432, 433, 537.3.1.1)	✓
7.10	**Presence of appropriate circuit charts, warning and other notices:**	
7.10.1	Provision of circuit charts/schedules or equivalent forms of information (514.9)	✓
7.10.2	Warning notice of method of isolation where live parts not capable of being isolated by a single device (514.11)	N/A
7.10.3	Periodic inspection and testing notice (514.12.1)	✓
7.10.4	RCD six-monthly test notice; where required (514.12.2)	✓
7.10.5	AFDD six-monthly test notice; where required	N/A

Created by NAPIT © Copyright NAPIT 2018
NAPIT Administration Centre, 4th Floor, Mill 3, Pleasley Vale Business Park, Mansfield, Nottinghamshire NG19 8RL
NA/EIC/001

Electrical Certificate *Installation/Modification* **Inspection Schedule**

for Domestic and Similar Premises up to 100 A Supply
Requirements for Electrical Installations - BS 7671:2018 (IET Wiring Regulations 18ᵗʰ Edition) All items inspections to confirm as appropriate, compliance with the relevant clauses in BS 7671:2018

NAPIT

NA/	7	6	5	4	3	2	1	0	0	0	0	2
EIC							Page		3	of	4	

7.10.6	Warning notice of non-standard (mixed) colours of conductors' present (514.14)	✓
7.11	Presence of labels to indicate the purpose of switchgear and protective devices (514.1.1; 514.8)	N/A

8.0 Circuits

8.1	Adequacy of conductors for current-carrying capacity with regard to type and nature of the installation (Section 523)	✓
8.2	Cable installation methods suitable for the location(s) and external influences (Section 522)	✓
8.3	Segregation/separation of Band I (ELV) and Band II (LV) circuits, and electrical and non-electrical services (528)	N/A
8.4	Cables correctly erected and supported throughout with protection against abrasion (Sections 521, 522)	✓
8.5	Provision of fire barriers, sealing arrangements where necessary (527.2)	✓
8.6	Non-sheathed cables enclosed throughout in conduit, ducting or trunking (521.10.1; 526.8)	N/A
8.7	Cables concealed under floors, above ceilings or in walls/partitions, adequately protected against damage (522.6.201, 522.6.202, 522.6.203; 522.6.204)	N/A
8.8	Conductors correctly identified by colour, lettering or numbering (Section 514)	✓
8.9	Presence, adequacy and correct termination of protective conductors (411.3.1.1; 543.1)	✓
8.10	Cables and conductors correctly connected, enclosed and with no undue mechanical strain (Section 526)	✓
8.11	No basic insulation of a conductor visible outside enclosure (526.8)	✓
8.12	Single-pole devices for switching or protection in line conductors only (132.14.1; 530.3.3; 643.6)	✓
8.13	Accessories not damaged, securely fixed, correctly connected, suitable for external influences (134.1.1; 512.2; Section 526)	✓
8.14	**Provision of additional protection/requirements by RCD not exceeding 30 mA**	
8.14.1	Socket-outlets rated at 32 A or less, unless exempt (411.3.3)	✓
8.14.2	Supplies for mobile equipment with a current rating not exceeding 32 A for use outdoors (411.3.3)	✓
8.14.3	Cables concealed in walls at a depth of less than 50 mm (522.6.202, 522.6.203)	✓
8.14.4	Cables concealed in walls/partitions containing metal parts regardless of depth (522.6.202; 522.6.203)	✓
8.14.5	Final circuits supplying luminaires within domestic (household) premises (411.3.4)	✓
8.15	**Presence of appropriate devices for isolation and switching correctly located including:**	
8.15.1	Means of switching off for mechanical maintenance (Section 464; 537.3.2)	✓
8.15.2	Emergency switching (465.1; 537.3.3)	N/A
8.15.3	Functional switching, for control of parts of the installation and current-using equipment (463.1; 537.3.1)	✓
8.15.4	Firefighter's switches (537.4)	N/A

9.0 Current-Using Equipment (Permanently Connected)

9.1	Equipment not damaged, securely fixed and suitable for external influences (134.1.1; 416.2; 512.2)	✓
9.2	Provision of overload and/or undervoltage protection e.g. for rotating machines, if required (Sections 445, 552)	N/A
9.3	Installed to minimize the build-up of heat and restrict the spread of fire (421.1.4; 559.4.1)	✓
9.4	Adequacy of working space. Accessibility to equipment (132.12; 513.1)	✓

10.0 Location(s) Containing A Bath Or Shower (Section 701)

10.1	30 mA RCD protection for all LV circuits, equipment suitable for the zones, supplementary bonding (where required) etc.	✓

11.0 Other Part 7 Special Installations or Locations (list all other special installations or locations present)

11.1	**List all other special installations or locations present, if any. (Record separately the results of particular inspections applied)**	
11.2	N/A	N/A
11.3	N/A	N/A
11.4	N/A	
11.5	N/A	

12.0 Schedule of Test Results to be recorded on Schedule of Test Result

12.1	External earth loop impedance, Ze	✓	12.9	Insulation Resistance between Live Conductors	✓
12.2	Installation earth electrode	N/A	12.10	Insulation Resistance between Live Conductors & Earth	✓
12.3	Prospective fault current, Ipf	✓	12.11	Polarity (prior to energisation)	✓
12.4	Continuity of Earth Conductors	✓	12.12	Polarity (after energisation) including phase sequence	✓
12.5	Continuity of Circuit Protective Conductors	✓	12.13	Earth Fault Loop Impedance	✓
12.6	Continuity of Ring Final Circuit	✓	12.14	RCDs/RCBOs including selectivity	✓
12.7	Continuity of Protective Bonding Conductors	✓	12.15	Functional testing of RCD devices	✓
12.8	Volt drop verified	N/A	12.16	Functional testing of AFDD(s) devices	N/A

Inspector's Name:	Mr Toptech	Signature:	*Top Tech*
Date:	14/04/2020		

Electrical Certificate Installation/Modification Test Schedule

for Domestic and Similar Premises up to 100 A Supply

Requirements for Electrical Installations
BS 7671:2018 (IET Wiring Regulations 18th Edition)

NA/ 1 2 3 4 5 6 7 0 0 0 0 1
EIC Page 4 of 4

Client M Smith

Installation Address 101 Park Road, Park Lane, Parkford
Postcode PAK1 2PF

Distribution board details - Complete in every case

Complete only if the distribution board is not connected directly to the origin of the installation

Location	Kitchen	
Designation	DB 1	
Num. of ways	8x sp	

Supply to distribution board is from
Overcurrent protective device for the distribution circuit:
No. of phases N/A
Type N/A   BS(EN) N/A
Nominal Voltage N/A   Rating N/A   A
N/A
Supply polarity confirmed ✓   Phase sequence confirmed ✓

Characteristics at this distribution board
Associated RCD(if any): BS (EN)
N/A
Zs 0.35 Ω No. of poles N/A
Ia 0.7 kA IΔn N/A mA
Time delay (if applicable) N/A

Test instrument serial number(s)
Loop impedance 77777
Operating at 1 IΔn N/A ms Insulation resistance 77777
Operating at 5 IΔn N/A ms Continuity 77777
RCD 77777

CIRCUIT DETAILS

Circuit No. and Line No.	Circuit designation	Type of wiring	Ref. method	No. of points served	Circuit conductors csa L/N (mm2)	Circuit conductors csa CPC (mm2)	Maximum disconnection time (BS 7671)	BS EN Number	Type No.	Rating (A)	Breaking capacity (kA)	RCD operating current IΔn (mA)	BS 7671 Max permitted value Zs (Ω)
1	Skt Ring Circuit	A	C	12	2.5	1.5	0.4	61009	B	32	6	30	1.1
2	Cooker - Hob	A	C	1	6	2.5	0.4	61009	B	32	6	30	1.1
3	Lights Up	A	C	6	1.5	1	0.4	61009	B	6	6	30	5.82
4	Lights Down	A	C	12	1.5	1	0.4	61009	B	6	6	30	5.82
5	Electric Shower	A	C	1	6	2.5	0.4	61009	B	32	6	30	1.1
6	Skt Radial	A	C	9	2.5	1.5	0.4	61009	B	20	6	30	1.75
7	Sub Main to -Shed	A	C	1	6	2.5	5	60898	B	40	6	N/A	0.87
8	Spare												

TEST RESULTS

Circuit No. and Line No.	Ring final circuits only (measured end to end) r1	m	r2	Fig θ check (✓)	All circuits to be completed using R1+R2 or R2 at each R1+R2	R2	Test voltage V	Insulation resistance (Record lower reading) L-L / L-N M(Ω)	L-E / N-E M(Ω)	Polarity (✓)	Max Measured Zs (Ω)	RCD testing At IΔn 1 IΔn ms	At 5 IΔn ms	30mA or below 5 IΔn ms	AFDD RCD (✓)	Manual test button operation RCD (✓)
1	0.66	0.6	1.1	✓	0.42	NA	500	>500	>500	✓	0.77	22	NA	NA	✓	NA
2	NA	NA	NA	✓	0.23	NA	500	>500	>500	✓	0.55	22	NA	NA	✓	NA
3	NA	NA	NA	✓	0.67	NA	500	>500	>500	✓	1.2	22	NA	NA	✓	NA
4	NA	NA	NA	✓	0.78	NA	500	>500	>500	✓	1.13	22	NA	NA	✓	NA
5	NA	NA	NA	✓	0.22	NA	500	>500	>500	✓	0.56	22	NA	NA	✓	NA
6	NA	NA	NA	✓	0.39	NA	500	>500	>500	✓	0.71	22	NA	NA	✓	NA
7	NA	NA	NA	✓	0.3	NA	500	>500	>500	✓	0.67	NA	NA	NA	NA	NA

Details of circuits and/or installed equipment vulnerable to damage when testing
USB skts

Date(s) dead testing 14/04/2020 **To** 14/04/2020
Date(s) live testing 14/04/2020 **To** 14/04/2020

Tested by: Name (capital letters) Mr Toptech   **Position** Electrician   **Date** 14/04/2020
Signature Top Tech

Wiring Types: A PVC/PVC B PVC cables in metallic Conduit C PVC cables in non-metallic Conduit D PVC cables in metallic Trunking E PVC cables in non-metallic Trunking F PVC/SWA cables G SWA/XPLE cables H Mineral Insulated O Other

Created by NAPIT © Copyright NAPIT 2018
NAPIT Administration Centre, 4th Floor, Mill 3, Pleasley Vale Business Park, Mansfield, Nottinghamshire NG19 8RL

NAE/EIC/001

NAPIT
Electrical Installation
Condition Report

For Domestic and Similar Premises with up to 100 A Supply

Requirements for Electrical Installations – BS 7671:2018
[IET Wiring Regulations 18th Edition]

NA/EICR/D001 (V1)

NAPIT

NAPIT Administration Centre
4th Floor, Mill 3
Pleasley Vale Business Park
Mansfield
Nottinghamshire
NG19 8RL

www.napit.org.uk   0345 543 0330   info@napit.org.uk

NAPIT *Electrical Installation Condition Report*
For Domestic and Similar Premises with up to 100 A Supply

Notes for the person producing the Report:

1. This Report should only be used for reporting on the condition of an existing electrical installation, and not for the replacement of a consume unit/distribution board. An installation which was designed to an earlier edition of the Regulations and which does not fully comply with the current edition is not necessarily unsafe for continued use, or requires upgrading. Only damage, deterioration, defects, dangerous conditions and non-compliance with the requirements of the Regulations, which may give rise to danger, should be recorded.

2. The Report, normally comprising at least six pages, should include schedules of both the inspection and the test results. Additional pages may be necessary for other than a simple installation and for the 'Guidance for recipients'. The number of each page should be indicated, together with the total number of pages involved.

3. The reason for producing this Report, such as change of occupancy or landlord's periodic maintenance, should be identified in Section B.

4. Those elements of the installation that are covered by the Report and those that are not should be identified in Section D (Extent and limitations). These aspects should have been agreed with the person ordering the report and other interested parties before the inspection and testing commenced. Any operational limitations, such as inability to gain access to parts of the installation or an item of equipment, should also be recorded in Section D.

5. The maximum prospective value of fault current (I^{pf}) recorded should be the greater of either the prospective value of short-circuit current or the prospective value of earth fault current.

6. Where an installation has an alternative source of supply a further schedule of supply characteristics and earthing arrangements based upon Section I of this Report should be provided.

7. A summary of the condition of the installation in terms of safety should be clearly stated in Section E. Observations, if any, should be categorised in Section K using the coding C1 to C3 as appropriate. Any observation given a code C1 or C2 classification should result in the overall condition of the installation being reported as unsatisfactory.

8. Wherever practicable, **items classified as 'Danger present' (C1) should be made safe on discovery.**

9. Where this is not possible the owner or user should be given written notification as a matter of urgency.

10. Where an observation requires further investigation (FI) because the inspection has revealed an apparent deficiency which could not, owing to the extent or limitations of the inspection, be fully identified and further investigation may reveal a code C1 or C2 item, this should be recorded within Section K, given the code FI and marked as unsatisfactory in Section E.

11. If the space available for observations in Section K is insufficient, additional pages should be provided as necessary.

12. The date by which the next Electrical Installation Condition Report is recommended should be given in Section F. The interval between inspections should take into account the type and usage of the installation and its overall condition.

Electrical Installation Condition Report

Requirements for Electrical Installations - BS7671:2018
NAPIT (IET Wiring Regulations 18th Edition)

Information for recipients:

This Report is an important and valuable document which should be retained for future reference.

The purpose of this report is to confirm, so far as reasonably practicable, whether or not the electrical installation is in a satisfactory condition for continued service (see Section E). The report should identify any damage, deterioration, defects and/or conditions which may give rise to danger (see Section K).

The person ordering the report should have received the original report and the inspector should have retained a duplicate.

The original Report should be retained in a safe place and be made available to any person inspecting or undertaking work on the electrical installation in the future. If the property is vacated, this report will provide the new owner / occupier with details of the condition of the electrical installation at the time the report was issued.

Where the installation incorporates residual current devices (RCDs) there should be a notice at or near the devices stating that they should be tested every 6 months. For safety reasons it is important that these instructions are followed.

Section D (Extent and Limitations) should identify fully the extent of the installation covered by this report and any limitations on the inspection and testing. The Inspector should have agreed these aspects with the person ordering the report and with other interested parties (licencing authority, insurance company, mortgage provider and the like) before the inspection was carried out.

Some operational limitations such as inability to gain access to parts of the installation or an item of equipment may have been encountered during the inspection. The inspector should have noted these in Section D.

For items classified in Section K as C1 ("Danger Present"), the safety of those using the installation is at risk, and it is recommended that a skilled person or persons competent in electrical installation work undertakes the necessary remedial work immediately.

For items classified in Section K as C2 ("Potentially Dangerous"), the safety of those using the installation may be at risk and it is recommended that a skilled person or persons competent in electrical installation work undertakes the necessary remedial work as a matter of urgency.

Where it has been stated in Section K that an observation requires further investigation code FI the inspection has revealed an apparent deficiency which may result on a code C1 or C2 could not, due to the extent or limitations of this inspection, be fully identified. Such observations should be investigated as soon as possible. A further examination of the installation will be necessary, to determine the nature and extent of the apparent deficiency (see Section F).

For safety reasons, the electrical installation should be re-inspected at appropriate intervals by a skilled person or persons competent in such work. The recommended date by which the next inspection is due is stated in Section F of the report under 'Recommendations' and on label at or near to the consumer unit/distribution board.

Created by NAPIT © Copyright NAPIT 2018
NAPIT Administration Centre, 4th Floor, Mill 3, Pleasley Vale Business Park, Mansfield, Nottinghamshire NG19 8RL

NA/EICR/001

Electrical Installation Condition Report

for Domestic and Similar Premises up to 100 A Supply
Requirements for Electrical Installations
BS 7671:2018 (IET Wiring Regulations 18th Edition)

NA/ | 1 | 2 | 3 | 4 | 5 | 6 | 7 | 0 | 0 | 0 | 0 | 1
EICR   Page 1 of 5

A   Details of the Installation

Client   M Smith

Installation   House Dwelling

Address   101 Park Road
Park Lane
Parkford

Address   Same as client

Postcode   PAK1 2PF

Postcode

B   Reason for producing this report
This form is to be used only for reporting on the condition of an existing installation.

Rented accommodation, Insurance purposes.

Date(s) on which the inspection and testing were carried out   14/04/2020   to   14/04/2020

C   Details of installation which is the subject of this report

Description of premises   Domestic ☑   Commercial ☐   Industrial ☐   Other (please specify) N/A

Estimated age of the wiring system   10   years

Evidence of alterations or addition   Yes ☑   No ☐   Not apparent ☐   if 'Yes', estimated   3   years

Records of installation available   Yes ☑   No ☐   Records held by   client

Date of last inspection   14/04/2015   Electrical Installation Certificate No. or previous Inspection Report No.   444444444000001

D

Extent of electrical installation covered by this report:

All circuits from D/B 1

Agreed Limitations and Operational Limitations (Regulations 653.2)

Operational limitations including the reasons see page no   N/A   of   N/A   Agreed with: N/A

The inspection and testing detailed within this report and accompanying schedule has been carried out in accordance with BS 7671: 2018 amended to   2020

It should be noted that cables concealed within the trunkings and conduits, under floors, in roof spaces and generally within the fabric of the building or underground have not been inspected unless specifically agreed between the client and inspector prior to the inspection. An inspection should be made within an accessible roof space housing other electrical equipment.

E   Summary of the condition of the installation

General conditions of the installation (in terms of safety)

Good condition with two recommendations

Overall assessment of the installation in terms of its suitability for continued use   SATISFACTORY ☑   *UNSATISFACTORY ☐

*An UNSATISFACTORY assessment indicates that dangerous (code C1), or potentially dangerous (code C2), Further investigation (code FI) conditions have been identified

F   Recommendations

Where the overall assessment of the suitability of the installation for continued use above is stated as UNSATISFACTORY I/we recommend that any observations classified as 'Danger present' (code C1) or 'Potentially dangerous' (code C2) are acted upon as a matter of urgency. Investigation without delay is recommended for observations identified as 'Further Investigation required' (code FI). Observations classified as 'Improvement recommended' (code C3) should be given due consideration. Subject to the necessary remedial action being taken, I/we recommend that the installation is further inspected and tested by   14/04/2025   (date)

G   Declaration

I/we being the person(s) responsible for the inspection and the testing of the electrical installation (as indicated by my/our signatures below), particulars of which are described above, having exercised reasonable skill and care when carrying out the inspection and testing hereby declare that the information in this report, including the observations and the attached schedules, provides an accurate assessment of the condition of the electrical installation taking into account the stated extent and limitations in section D of this report.

Company	Techsafe		Inspected and tested by	Authorised for issue by
Membership No.	1234567	Name:	Mr Toptech	Mr Toptech
Address	77 Street Top road	Signature:	*Top Tech*	*Top Tech*
		Position:	Electrician	Electrician
Postcode	TR1 1TR	Date:	14/04/2020	14/04/2020

H   Schedule(s)

1 schedule(s) of inspection and 1 schedule(s) of test results are attached.

The attached schedule(s) are part of this document and this report is valid only when they are attached to it.

Created by NAPIT © Copyright NAPIT 2018
NAPIT Administration Centre, 4th Floor, Mill 3, Pleasley Vale Business Park, Mansfield, Nottinghamshire NG19 8RL

NA/EICR/001

Electrical Installation Condition Report

for Domestic and Similar Premises up to 100 A Supply
Requirements for Electrical Installations
BS 7671:2018 (IET Wiring Regulations 18th Edition)

NAPIT

| NA/ | 1 | 2 | 3 | 4 | 5 | 6 | 7 | 0 | 0 | 0 | 0 | 1 |

EICR   Page **2** of **5**

I Supply characteristics and earthing arrangements

Earthing Arrangements TN-S ☐ TN-C-S ☑ TT ☐ Other ☐ Please specify N/A

Number & Type of live conductors AC ☑ DC ☐ No. of phases 1 No. of wires 2

Nature of Supply Parameters (Note: [1] **by enquiry,** [2] **by enquiry or by measurement)**

Nominal voltage, U/U_0 [1] 230 v   Nominal frequency, f [1] 50 Hz   Confirmation of polarity ☑

Prospective fault current, I_{pf} [2] 0.7 kA   External loop impedance, Z_e [2] 0.35 Ω Or Z_{db} Source of Circuit N/A

Supply Protective Device BS (EN) 1361   Type 2   Rated Current 100 A

Other Sources of Supply (as detailed on attached schedule) N/A

J Particulars of installation referred to in this report

Details of installation Earth Electrode (where applicable) Type (e.g. rod(s), tape etc) N/A   **Means of Earthing**

Location N/A   Electrode resistance to earth N/A Ω   Distributors facility ☑ Installation Earth Electrode ☐

Main Protective Conductors	Material	csa	(✓) or Value		Maximum Demand (load) 80 Amps ☑ KVA ☐

Earthing Conductor Copper 16 ☑ N/A Ω   (connection / continuity) (✓) or Value (✓) or Value

Protective Bonding Conductor (to extraneous-conductive-parts) Copper 10 ☑   Water installation ☑ N/A Ω To structural steel ☐ Ω

Main Supply Conductor Copper 25   Gas installation pipes ☑ N/A Ω To lightning protection ☐ Ω

Oil installation pipes ☐ Ω Other ☐ Ω

Main Switch Location DB 1 kitchen

Fuse/device rating or setting Switch   A Voltage rating 230 V   BS(EN) 60947-3   No. of Poles 2   Current Rating 100 A

If RCD main switch: Rated residual operating current I Δn N/A mA   Rated time delay N/A ms   Measured operating trip time N/A ms

K Observations

Referring to the attached schedule of inspection and test results, and subject to the limitations at Section D.

☐ No remedial work required

☑ The following observations are made

Explanation of codes

C1 Danger present. Risk of Injury. Immediate remedial action required.

C2 Potentially dangerous. Urgent remedial action required.

C3 Improvement recommended.

FI Further Investigation required without delay

Item No.	Observations	Code
1	Consumer Unit has restricted access	C3
2	Sockets mounted too low	C3

One of the above codes, as appropriate, has been allocated to each of the observations made above and/or any attached observation sheets to indicate to the person(s) responsible for the installation the degree of urgency for remedial action.

Danger present. Risk of Injury. Immediate remedial action required.	
Potentially dangerous. Urgent remedial action required.	
Improvement recommended.	1, 2.
Further Investigation required without delay	

Electrical Installation Condition Report Inspection Schedule

for Domestic and Similar Premises up to 100 A Supply
Requirements for Electrical Installations - BS 7671:2018 (IET Wiring Regulations 18ᵗʰ Edition) All items inspections to confirm as appropriate, compliance with the relevant clauses in BS 7671:2018

NA/	1	2	3	4	5	6	7	0	0	0	0	1
EICR						Page	3	of	5			

Outcomes

Acceptable condition:	Unacceptable condition: State C1 or C2	Improvement recommended: C3	Further Investigation: FI	Not Verified: N/V	Limitation:	Not Applicable: N/A

In the outcome column use the codes above. Provide additional comment where appropriate. C1/C2/C3 and FI coded items to be recorded in section K of the condition report.

Item No.	Description	Outcome
1.0 External Condition Of Intake Equipment (Visual Inspection Only) Where inadequacies are encountered, it is recommended that the person ordering the report informs the appropriate authority		
1.1	Service cable	✓
1.2	Service head	✓
1.3	Earthing arrangement	✓
1.4	Meter tails	✓
1.5	Metering equipment	✓
1.6	Isolator (where present)	✓
2.0	Presence Of Adequate Arrangements For Other Sources Such As Microgenerators (551.6; 551.7)	N/A
3.0 Earthing / Bonding Arrangements (411.3; Chap 54)		
3.1	Presence and condition of distributor's earthing arrangement (542.1.2.1; 542.1.2.2)	✓
3.2	Presence and condition of earth electrode connection where applicable (542.1.2.3)	N/A
3.3	Provision of earthing/bonding labels at all appropriate locations (514.13.1)	✓
3.4	Confirmation of earthing conductor size (542.3; 543.1.1)	✓
3.5	Accessibility and condition of earthing conductor at MET arrangement (543.3.2)	✓
3.6	Confirmation of main protective bonding conductor sizes (544.1)	✓
3.7	Condition and accessibility of main protective bonding conductor/connections (543.3.2; 544.1.2)	✓
3.8	Accessibility and condition of other protective bonding connections (543.3.1; 543.3.2)	N/A
4.0 Consumer Unit(s) / Distribution Board(s)		
4.1	Adequacy of working space/accessibility to consumer unit/distribution board (132.12; 513.1)	⊕
4.2	Security of fixing (134.1.1)	✓
4.3	Condition of enclosure(s) in terms of IP rating etc (416.2)	✓
4.4	Condition of enclosure(s) in terms of fire rating etc (421.1.201; 526.5)	✓
4.5	Enclosure not damaged/deteriorated so as to impair safety (651.2)	✓
4.6	Presence of main linked switch (as required by 462.1.201)	✓
4.7	Operation of main switches (functional check) (643.10)	✓
4.8	Manual operation of circuit-breakers and RCD(s) to prove disconnection (643.10)	✓
4.9	Correct identification of circuit details and protective devices (514.8.1; 514.9.1)	✓
4.10	Presence of RCD six-monthly test notice at or near consumer unit/distribution board (514.12.2)	✓
4.11	Presence of non-standard (mixed) cable colour warning notice at or near consumer unit/distribution board (514.14)	✓
4.12	Presence of alternative supply warning notice at or near consumer unit/distribution board (514.15)	N/A
4.13	Presence of other required labelling (please specify) (Section 514)	N/A
4.14	Compatibility of protective devices, bases and other components; correct type and rating (No signs of unacceptable thermal damage, arcing or overheating) (411.3.2; 411.4; 411.5; 411.6; section 432.433)	✓
4.15	Single-pole switching or protective devices in line conductor only (132.14.1; 530.3.3)	✓
4.16	Protection against mechanical damage where cables enter consumer unit/distribution board (132.14.1; 522.8.1; 522.8.5; 522.8.11)	✓
4.17	Protection against electromagnetic effects where cables enter consumer unit/distribution board/enclosures (521.5.1)	✓
4.18	RCD(s) provided for fault protection - includes RCBOs (411.4.204; 411.5.2; 531.2)	✓
4.19	RCD(s) provided for additional protection/requirements - includes RCBOs (411.3.3; 415.1)	✓
4.20	Confirmation of indication that SPD is functional (651.4)	N/A
4.21	Confirmation that ALL conductor connections, including connections to busbars, are correctly located in terminals and are tight and secure (526.1)	✓
4.22	Adequate arrangements where a generating set operates as a switched alternative to the public supply (551.6)	N/A
4.23	Adequate arrangements where a generating set operates in parallel with the public supply (551.7)	N/A
5.0 Final Circuits		
5.1	Identification of conductors (514.3.1)	✓
5.2	Cables correctly supported throughout their run (521.10.202; 522.8.5)	✓
5.3	Condition of insulation of live parts (416.1)	✓

NA/EICR/001

NAPIT

for Domestic and Similar Premises up to 100 A Supply
Requirements for Electrical Installations - BS 7671:2018 (IET Wiring Regulations 18th Edition) All items inspections to confirm as appropriate, compliance with the relevant clauses in BS 7671:2018

NA/	1	2	3	4	5	6	7	0	0	0	0	1
EICR									Page	4	of	5

5.4	Non-sheathed cables protected by enclosure in conduit, ducting or trunking. Integrity of containment (521.10.1)	✓
5.4.1	To include the integrity of conduit and trunking systems (metallic and plastic)	
5.5	Adequacy of cables for current-carrying capacity with regard for the type and nature of installation (Section 523)	✓
5.6	Coordination between conductors and overload protective devices (433.1; 533.2.1)	✓
5.7	Adequacy of protective devices: type and rated current for fault protection (411.3)	✓
5.8	Presence and adequacy of circuit protective conductors (433.3.1; Section 543)	✓
5.9	Wiring system(s) appropriate for the type and nature of the installation and external influences (Section 522)	✓
5.10	Concealed cables installed in prescribed zones (see Section D. Extent and limitations) (522.6.202)	✓
5.11	Cables concealed under floors, above ceilings or in walls/partitions, adequately protected against damage (see Section D. Extent and limitations) (522.6.204)	✓
5.12	**Provision of additional requirements for protection by RCD not exceeding 30 mA**	
5.12.1	For all socket-outlets of rating 32 A or less, unless an exception is permitted (411.3.3)	✓
5.12.2	For the supply of mobile equipment not exceeding 32 A rating for use outdoors (411.3.3)	✓
5.12.3	For cables concealed in walls at a depth of less than 50 mm (522.6.202; 522.6.203)	✓
5.12.4	For cables concealed in walls/partitions containing metal parts regardless of depth (522.6.203)	✓
5.12.5	For circuits supplying luminaires within domestic (household) premises (411.3.4)	✓
5.13	Provision of fire barriers, sealing arrangements and protection against thermal effects (Section 527)	✓
5.14	Band II cables segregated/separated from Band I cables (528.1)	✓
5.15	Cables segregated/separated from communications cabling (528.2)	✓
5.16	Cables segregated/separated from non-electrical services (528.3)	✓
5.17	**Termination of cables at enclosures - indicate extent of sampling in Section D of the report (Section 526)**	
5.17.1	Connections soundly made and under no undue strain (526.6)	✓
5.17.2	No basic insulation of a conductor visible outside enclosure (526.8)	✓
5.17.3	Connections of live conductors adequately enclosed (526.5)	✓
5.17.4	Adequately connected at point of entry to enclosure (glands, bushes etc.) (522.8.5)	✓
5.18	Condition of accessories including socket-outlets, switches and joint boxes (651.2(v))	✓
5.19	Suitability of accessories for external influences (512.2)	✓
5.20	Adequacy of working space/accessibility to equipment (132.12; 513.1)	✓
5.21	Single-pole switching or protective devices in line conductors only (132.14.1, 530.3.3)	✓

6.0 Location(s) Containing A Bath Or Shower

6.1	Additional protection for all low voltage (LV) circuits by RCD not exceeding 30 mA (701.411.3.3)	✓
6.2	Where used as a protective measure, requirements for SELV or PELV met (701.414.4.5)	✓
6.3	Shaver sockets comply with BS EN 61558-2-5 formerly BS 3535 (701.512.3)	✓
6.4	Presence of supplementary bonding conductors, unless not required by BS 7671:2018 (701.415.2)	✓
6.5	Low voltage (e.g. 230 volt) socket-outlets sited at least 3 m from zone 1 (701.512.3)	✓
6.6	Suitability of equipment for external influences for installed location in terms of IP rating (701.512.2)	✓
6.7	Suitability of accessories and controlgear etc. for a particular zone (701.512.3)	✓
6.8	Suitability of current-using equipment for particular position within the location (701.55)	✓

7.0 Other Part 7 Special Installations Or Locations

7.1	List all other special installation or locations, if any (record seperately the results of particular inspections applied). See sheet:	

8.0 Schedule of Test   Results to be recorded on Schedule of Test Result

8.1	External earth loop impedance, Ze	✓	8.9	Insulation Resistance between Live Conductors	✓
8.2	Installation earth electrode		8.10	Insulation Resistance between Live Conductors & Earth	✓
8.3	Prospective fault current, Ipf	✓	8.11	Polarity (prior to energisation)	✓
8.4	Continuity of Earth Conductors	✓	8.12	Polarity (after energisation) including phase sequence	✓
8.5	Continuity of Circuit Protective Conductors	✓	8.13	Earth Fault Loop Impedance	✓
8.6	Continuity of Ring Final Circuit	✓	8.14	RCDs/RCBOs including selectivity	✓
8.7	Continuity of Protective Bonding Conductors	✓	8.15	Functional testing of RCD devices	✓
8.8	Volt drop verified		8.16	Functional testing of AFDD(s) devices	

Inspector's Name:	Mr Toptech
Date:	14/04/2020

Signature: *Top Tech*

NAPIT Certificates and Reports

Electrical Installation Condition Report Test Schedule

for Domestic and Similar Premises up to 100 A Supply

Requirements for Electrical Installations
BS 7671:2018 (IET Wiring Regulations 18th Edition)

NAV 1 2 3 4 5 6 7 0 0 0 0 0 1
EICR Page 5 of 5

Client M Smith

Installation Address 101 Park Road, Park Lane, Parkford **Postcode** PAK1 2PF

Distribution-board details – Complete in every case

Location	Kitchen
Designation	DB 1
Num. of ways	8x sp

Complete only if the distribution board is not connected directly to the origin of the installation

Supply to distribution board is from

Overcurrent protective device for the distribution circuit:	No. of phases	N/A
	Nominal Voltage	N/A
	Supply polarity confirmed	✓

	Type	N/A	BS(EN)	N/A
	Rating	N/A	A
	Phase sequence confirmed	✓

Characteristics at this distribution board

Associated RCD(if any): BS (EN)

Ze	N/A	Ω	No. of poles	N/A
Zs	0.35		Above 30mA	N/A
IΔn	0.7	kA	IΔn	N/A
Time delay (if applicable)		N/A	ms

Operating at 1 IΔn	N/A	ms
Operating at 30mA or below	
Operating at 5 IΔn	N/A	ms
30mA or below	

Test instrument serial number(s)

Loop impedance	77777
Insulation resistance	77777
Continuity	77777
RCD	77777

CIRCUIT DETAILS

Circuit No. and Line No.	Circuit designation	Type of wiring	Ref. method	No. of points served	Circuit conductors csa L/N (mm2)	Circuit conductors csa CPC (mm2)	Maximum disconnection time (BS 7671) (s)	BS EN Number	Type No.	Rating (A)	Breaking capacity (kA)	RCD operating current IΔn (mA)	BS 7671 Max permitted earth fault Zs 80% (Ω)
1	Skt Ring Circuit	A	C	12	2.5	1.5	0.4	61009	B	32	6	30	1.1
2	Cooker - Hob	A	C	1	6	2.5	0.4	61009	B	32	6	30	1.1
3	Lights Up	A	C	6	1.5	1	0.4	61009	B	6	6	30	5.82
4	Lights Down	A	C	12	1	1.5	0.4	61009	B	6	6	30	5.82
5	Electric Shower	A	C	1	6	2.5	0.4	61009	B	32	6	30	1.1
6	Skt Radial	A	C	9	2.5	1.5	0.4	61009	B	20	6	30	1.75
7	Sub Main to -Shed	A	C	1	6	2.5	5	60898	B	40	6	N/A	0.87
8	Spare												

TEST RESULTS

Circuit No. and Line No.	Continuity Ring final circuits only (measured end to end) r1	m r_n	r2	Circuit impedance Ω All returns to be completed using R1/R2 or R2, not both R1+R2	R2	Fig 8 check ✓	Insulation resistance (Record lower reading) Test voltage V	L-L / L-N MΩ	L-E / N-E MΩ	Polarity ✓	Max. Measured Zs (Ω)	RCD testing Above 30mA IΔn ms	30mA or below 5 IΔn ms	RCD ✓	AFDD ✓	Manual test button operation ✓
1	0.66	0.6	1.1	0.42	NA	✓	500	>500	>500	✓	0.77	NA	22	✓		NA
2	NA	NA	NA	0.23	✓	✓	500	>500	>500	✓	0.55	NA	22	✓		NA
3	NA	NA	NA	0.67	✓	✓	500	>500	>500	✓	1.2	NA	22	✓		NA
4	NA	NA	NA	0.78	✓	✓	500	>500	>500	✓	1.13	NA	22	✓		NA
5	NA	NA	NA	0.22	✓	✓	500	>500	>500	✓	0.56	NA	22	✓		NA
6	NA	NA	NA	0.39	✓	✓	500	>500	>500	✓	0.71	NA	22	✓		NA
7	NA	NA	NA	0.3	✓	✓	500	>500	>500	✓	0.67	NA	NA	NA	NA	

Details of circuits and/or installed equipment vulnerable to damage when testing Date(s) dead testing 14/04/2020   To 14/04/2020   Date(s) live testing 14/04/2020   To 14/04/2020

USB skts

Tested by: Name (capital letters) Mr Toptech   **Position** Electrician   **Date** 14/04/2020   **Signature** Top Tech   NA

Wiring Types : A PVC/PVC 'B PVC cables in metallic Conduit 'C PVC cables in non-metallic Conduit 'D PVC cables in metallic Trunking'E PVC cables in non-metallic Trunking'F PVC/SWA cables 'G SWA/XPLE cables 'H Mineral Insulated 'O Other

Created by NAPIT © Copyright NAPIT 2018
NAPIT Administration Centre, 4th Floor, Mill 3, Pleasley Vale Business Park, Mansfield, Nottinghamshire NG19 8RL

NAE/EICR/001

NAPIT
Minor Electrical
Installation Works
Single/Double Circuit
Certificate

**Requirements for Electrical Installations – BS 7671:2018
[IET Wiring Regulations 18th Edition]**

NA/MEIWS/DC/001 (V1)

NAPIT

NAPIT Administration Centre
4th Floor, Mill 3
Pleasley Vale Business Park
Mansfield
Nottinghamshire
NG19 8RL

www.napit.org.uk   0345 543 0330   info@napit.org.uk

Minor Electrical Installation Works
Single/Double Circuit Certificate

Notes for the person producing the Certificate:

The Minor Electrical Installation Works Single/Double Circuit Certificate is intended to be used for additions and alterations to an installation that do not extend to the provision of a new circuit (unless a schedule of inspections is added). Examples include the addition of socket-outlets or lighting points to an existing circuit, the relocation of a light switch, etc.

This Certificate may also be used for the replacement of equipment such as accessories or luminaires, but not for the replacement of distribution boards or similar items. Appropriate inspection and testing, however, should always be carried out irrespective of the extent of the work undertaken.

NAPIT

Minor *Electrical Installation* Works / Double Circuit Certificate

Requirements for Electrical Installations
BS 7671:2018 (IET Wiring Regulations 18th
Edition)

Information for recipients:

This safety Certificate for Minor Works has been issued to confirm that the electrical installation work to which it relates has been designed, constructed, inspected and tested in accordance with BS 7671
(the IET Wiring Regulations).

You should have received an original Certificate and the contractor should have retained a duplicate.

If you were the person ordering this work, but not the owner of the installation, you should pass this Certificate, or a copy of it, immediately to the owner.
The original Certificate is to be retained in a safe place and be shown to any person inspecting or undertaking work on the electrical installation in the future.

If you later vacate the property, this Certificate will demonstrate to the new owner that the minor electrical installation work carried out complied with the requirements of BS 7671 at the time the Certificate was issued.

For safety reasons the electrical installation will need to be re-inspected at appropriate intervals by a skilled person or persons, competent in such work.

If this work is domestic and notifiable you should also receive a 'Compliance with Building Regulations Declaration' within 30 days of the electrical installation being completed.

(For additions or alterations) cables concealed within trunking and conduits, or cables or conduits concealed under floors, in roof spaces and generally within the fabric of the building or underground may not have been inspected unless specifically agreed between the client and the inspector prior to the inspection.

Minor *Electrical Installation* Works / Double Circuit Certificate

NAPIT
Requirements for Electrical Installations
BS 7671:2018 (IET Wiring Regulations 18th Edition)

NA/	1	2	3	4	5	6	0	0	0	0	0	1
MEIWSC								Page	1	of	3	

1 Details of the Installation

Client	M Smith	Installation	House Dwelling
Address	101 Park Road, Park Lane, Parkford	Address	Same as client
Postcode	PAK1 2PF	Postcode	--

Work type: New ☑ Addition ☐ Alteration ☐ ☐

Description of installation work covered by this certificate: New kitchen ring main sockets x 6

Records Available Yes ☐ No ☑ — New cooker circuit x1

This installation has been carried out in accordance with BS 7671:2018 (IET Wiring Regulations), amended to **2020** — Date of original installation **1999**

Details of departures from BS 7671:2018 (regulations 120.3, 133.5). See page(s) **N/A**

Comments on the existing installation: good

2 Supply characteristics and earthing arrangements

Earthing Arrangements: TN-S ☐ TN-C-S ☑ TT ☐ Other ☐ Please specify N/A

Number & Type of live conductors: AC ☑ DC ☐ No. of phases **1** No. of wires **2**

Nature of Supply Parameters (Note: [1] by enquiry, [2] by enquiry or by measurement)

Nominal voltage, U/U_0 [1] **230** v — Nominal frequency, f [1] **50** H_z — Confirmation of polarity ☑

Prospective fault current, I_{pf} [2] **0.7** kA — External loop impedance, Z_e [2] **0.35** Ω — Or Z_{db} Source of Circuit **N/A**

Supply Protective Device BS (EN) **1361** — Type **2** — Rated Current **100** A

Other Sources of Supply (as detailed on attached schedule) **N/A**

3 Particulars of installation referred to in this certificate

Means of Earthing: Distributors facility ☑ Installation Earth Electrode ☐

Details of installation Earth Electrode (where applicable) Type (e.g. rod(s), tape etc) **NA**

Location **N/A** — Electrode resistance to earth **N/A** Ω

Main Protective Conductors	Material	csa	(✓) or Value	
Earthing Conductor	Copper	16	☑ N/A	Ω
Protective Bonding Conductor (to extraneous-conductive-parts)	Copper	25	☑	
Main Supply Conductor	Copper	25		

Maximum Demand (load) **80** Amps ☑ KVA ☐

(connection / continuity) (✓) or Value:
Water installation ☑ N/A Ω — To structural steel ☐ Ω
Gas installation pipes ☑ N/A Ω — To lightning protection ☐ Ω
Oil installation pipes ☐ N/A Ω — To installation pipes ☐ Ω

Main Switch Location **DB 1 kitchen**

Fuse/device rating or setting: Switch — A Voltage rating **230** V — BS(EN) **60947-3** — No. of Poles **2** — Current Rating **100** A

If RCD main switch: Rated residual operating current $I_{\Delta n}$ **NA** mA — Rated time delay **NA** ms — Measured operating trip time **N/A** ms

CIRCUIT DETAILS

Circuit No. and Line No.	Location of distribution board (DB) Kitchen / DB designator DB 1 / Circuit designation	Type of wiring	Ref. method	No. of points served	Circuit conductors csa Live (mm²)	CPC (mm²)	Maximum disconnection time (BS 7671)	BS EN Number	Type No.	Rating (A)	Breaking Capacity (kA)	RCD operating current IΔn (mA)	BS 7671 Max. permitted value Zs Ω	Other %
3	Skt Ring Circuit	A	C	8	2.5	1.5	0.4	61009	B	32	6	30	1.1	80
5	Cooker - Hob	A	C	1	6	2.5	0.4	61009	B	32	6	30	1.1	

Wiring Types: A PVC/PVC B PVC cables in metallic Conduit C PVC cables in non-metallic Conduit D PVC cables in metallic Trunking E PVC cables in non-metallic Trunking F PVC/SWA cables G SWA/XPLE cables H Mineral Insulated O Other

TEST RESULTS

Ring final circuits only (measured end to end) r_1	r_n	r_2	Figure 8 check (✓)	All circuits to be completed using R_1+R_2 or R_2, not both R_1+R_2	R_2	Test Voltage V	Insulation resistance (record lower reading) L/L, L/N (MΩ)	L/E, L/N, N/E (MΩ)	Polarity (✓)	Maximum measured Z_s (Ω)	Above 30mA at IΔn ms	30mA or below at 5 IΔn ms	RCD (✓)	AFDD (✓)	Test instrument serial number(s) / Details of circuits and / or installed equipment vulnerable to damage when testing
0.68	0.68	1.13	✓	0.4	NA	500	>1000	>1000	✓	0.78	N/A	22	✓	N/A	USB skts
N/A	N/A	N/A	N/A	0.3	NA	500	>1000	>1000	✓	0.67	N/A	22	✓	N/A	N/A

Loop imp. 7777 — Cont. 7777
Insul res. 7777 — RCD 7777

4 Declaration

Live testing date **04/04/2020**

Details of permitted exception (Regulation 411.3.3) Where applicable, a suitable risk assessment(s) must be attached to this certificate. — Risk assessment attached ☐

DECLARATION: For the Design, Construction & the Inspection and Testing of the Installation as described above

Company	Techsafe	Signature	*Top Tech*
Inspector Name	Toptech	Position	Electrician
Address	77 Street, Top road, TR1 1TR	Date	04/04/2020
		Member No	1234567

NEXT INSPECTION: I recommend that this installation is further inspected and tested after an interval of not more than **5** years /////ths or on change of occupancy if dwelling.

Minor *Electrical Installation* Works / Double Circuit Certificate

Inspection Schedule

Requirements for Electrical Installations - BS 7671:2018 (IET Wiring Regulations 18th Edition) All items inspections to confirm as appropriate, compliance with the relevant clauses in BS 7671:2018

NAPIT

Outcomes

Indicates an inspection has been carried out and the result is satisfactory		Indicates the inspection is not applicable to a particular item	(N/A)

1.0 External Condition Of Intake Equipment (Visual Inspection Only)

1.1	Service cable	✓
1.2	Service head	✓
1.3	Earthing arrangement	✓
1.4	Meter tails	✓
1.5	Metering equipment	✓
1.6	Isolator (where present)	✓

2.0 Parallel Or Switched Alternative Sources Of Supply

2.1	Adequate arrangements where a generating set operates as a switched alternative to the public supply (551.6)	(N/A)
2.2	Adequate arrangements where a generating set operates in parallel with the public supply (551.7)	(N/A)

3.0 Automatic Disconnection Of Supply, Presence And Adequacy Of Earthing And Protective Bonding Arrangements

3.1	Distributor's earthing arrangement (542.1.2.1; 542.1.2.2)	✓
3.2	Installation earth electrode (where applicable) (542.1.2.3)	(N/A)
3.3	Earthing conductor and connections, including accessibility (542.3; 543.3.2)	✓
3.4	Main protective bonding conductors and connections, including accessibility (411.3.1.2; 543.3.2; Section 544.1)	✓
3.5	Provision of safety electrical earthing/bonding labels at all appropriate locations (514.13)	✓
3.6	RCD(s) provided for fault protection (411.4.204; 411.5.3)	✓

4.0 Basic Protection, Presence And Adequacy Of Measures To Provide Basic Protection (Prevention Of Contact With Live Parts) Within The Installation

4.1	Insulation of live parts e.g. conductors completely covered with durable insulating material (416.1)	✓
4.2	Barriers or enclosures e.g. correct IP rating (416.2)	✓

5.0 Additional Protection, Presence And Effectiveness Of Additional Protection Methods

5.1	RCD(s) not exceeding 30 mA operating current (415.1; Part 7), see Item 8.14 of this schedule	✓
5.2	Supplementary bonding (415.2; Part 7)	(N/A)

6.0 Other Methods Of Protection, Presence And Effectiveness Of Methods Which Give Both Basic And Fault Protection

6.1	SELV system, including the source and associated circuits (Section 414)	(N/A)
6.2	PELV system, including the source and associated circuits (Section 414)	(N/A)
6.3	Double or reinforced insulation i.e. Class II or equivalent equipment and associated circuits (Section 412)	(N/A)
6.4	Electrical separation for one item of equipment e.g. shaver supply unit (Section 413)	(N/A)

7.0 Consumer Unit(s) / Distribution Board(s)

7.1	Adequacy of access and working space for items of electrical equipment including switchgear (132.12)	✓
7.2	Components are suitable according to assembly manufacturer's instructions or literature (536.4.203)	✓
7.3	Presence of linked main switch(es) (462.1.201)	✓
7.4	Isolators, for every circuit or group of circuits and all items of equipment (462.2)	✓
7.5	Suitability of enclosure(s) for IP and fire ratings (416.2; 421.1.6; 421.1.201; 526.5)	✓
7.6	Protection against mechanical damage where cables enter equipment (522.8.1; 522.8.5; 522.8.11)	✓
7.7	Confirmation that ALL conductor connections are correctly located in terminals and are tight and secure (526.1)	✓
7.8	Avoidance of heating effects where cables enter ferromagnetic enclosures e.g. steel (521.5)	✓
7.9	Selection of correct type and ratings of circuit protective devices for overcurrent and fault protection (411.3.2; 411.4, 411.5, 411.6; Sections 432, 433, 537.3.1.1)	✓
7.10	**Presence of appropriate circuit charts, warning and other notices:**	
7.10.1	Provision of circuit charts/schedules or equivalent forms of information (514.9)	✓
7.10.2	Warning notice of method of isolation where live parts not capable of being isolated by a single device (514.11)	✓
7.10.3	Periodic inspection and testing notice (514.12.1)	✓
7.10.4	RCD six-monthly test notice; where required (514.12.2)	✓
7.10.5	AFDD six-monthly test notice; where required	(N/A)
7.11	Presence of labels to indicate the purpose of switchgear and protective devices (514.1.1; 514.8)	✓
7.10.6	Warning notice of non-standard (mixed) colours of conductors' present (514.14)	✓

8.0 Circuits

Minor *Electrical Installation* Works / Double Circuit Certificate

Inspection Schedule

Requirements for Electrical Installations - BS 7671:2018 (IET Wiring Regulations 18th Edition) All items inspections to confirm as appropriate, compliance with the relevant clauses in BS 7671:2018

NA/	1	2	3	4	5	6	0	0	0	0	0	1
MEIWSC								Page	3	of	3	

8.1	Adequacy of conductors for current-carrying capacity with regard to type and nature of the installation (Section 523)	✓
8.2	Cable installation methods suitable for the location(s) and external influences (Section 522)	✓
8.3	Segregation/separation of Band I (ELV) and Band II (LV) circuits, and electrical and non-electrical services (528)	(n/a)
8.4	Cables correctly erected and supported throughout with protection against abrasion (Sections 521, 522)	✓
8.5	Provision of fire barriers, sealing arrangements where necessary (527.2)	✓
8.6	Non-sheathed cables enclosed throughout in conduit, ducting or trunking (521.10.1; 526.8)	(n/a)
8.7	Cables concealed under floors, above ceilings or in walls/partitions, adequately protected against damage (522.6.201, 522.6.202, 522.6.203; 522.6.204)	✓
8.8	Conductors correctly identified by colour, lettering or numbering (Section 514)	✓
8.9	Presence, adequacy and correct termination of protective conductors (411.3.1.1; 543.1)	✓
8.10	Cables and conductors correctly connected, enclosed and with no undue mechanical strain (Section 526)	✓
8.11	No basic insulation of a conductor visible outside enclosure (526.8)	✓
8.12	Single-pole devices for switching or protection in line conductors only (132.14.1; 530.3.3; 643.6)	✓
8.13	Accessories not damaged, securely fixed, correctly connected, suitable for external influences (134.1.1; 512.2; Section 526)	✓
8.14	**Provision of additional protection/requirements by RCD not exceeding 30 mA**	
8.14.1	Socket-outlets rated at 32 A or less, unless exempt (411.3.3)	✓
8.14.2	Supplies for mobile equipment with a current rating not exceeding 32 A for use outdoors (411.3.3)	(n/a)
8.14.3	Cables concealed in walls at a depth of less than 50 mm (522.6.202, 522.6.203)	✓
8.14.4	Cables concealed in walls/partitions containing metal parts regardless of depth (522.6.202; 522.6.203)	✓
8.14.5	Final circuits supplying luminaires within domestic (household) premises (411.3.4)	(n/a)
8.15	**Presence of appropriate devices for isolation and switching correctly located including:**	
8.15.1	Means of switching off for mechanical maintenance (Section 464; 537.3.2)	✓
8.15.2	Emergency switching (465.1; 537.3.3)	(n/a)
8.15.3	Functional switching, for control of parts of the installation and current-using equipment (463.1; 537.3.1)	✓
8.15.4	Firefighter's switches (537.4)	(n/a)

9.0 Current-Using Equipment (Permanently Connected)

9.1	Equipment not damaged, securely fixed and suitable for external influences (134.1.1; 416.2; 512.2)	✓
9.2	Provision of overload and/or undervoltage protection e.g. for rotating machines, if required (Sections 445, 552)	(n/a)
9.3	Installed to minimize the build-up of heat and restrict the spread of fire (421.1.4; 559.4.1)	✓
9.4	Adequacy of working space. Accessibility to equipment (132.12; 513.1)	✓

10.0 Location(s) Containing A Bath Or Shower (Section 701)

10.1	30 mA RCD protection for all LV circuits, equipment suitable for the zones, supplementary bonding (where required) etc.	(n/a)

11.0 Other Part 7 Special Installations or Locations (list all other special installations or locations present)

11.1	List all other special installations or locations present, if any. (Record separately the results of particular inspections applied)

12.0 Schedule of Test Results to be recorded on Schedule of Test Result

12.1	External earth loop impedance, Ze	✓	12.9	Insulation Resistance between Live Conductors	✓
12.2	Installation earth electrode	(n/a)	12.10	Insulation Resistance between Live Conductors & Earth	✓
12.3	Prospective fault current Ipf	✓	12.11	Polarity (prior to energisation)	✓
12.4	Continuity of Earth Conductors	✓	12.12	Polarity (after energisation) including phase sequence	✓
12.5	Continuity of Circuit Protective Conductors	✓	12.13	Earth Fault Loop Impedance	✓
12.6	Continuity of ring final circuit	✓	12.14	RCDs / RCBOs including selectivity	✓
12.7	Continuity of Protective Bonding Conductors	✓	12.15	Functional testing of RCD(s)	✓
12.8	Volt drop verified	✓	12.16	Functional testing of AFDD(s)	(n/a)

Inspector's Name:	Toptech	Signature: *Top Tech*
Date:	14/04/2020	

Notes

N/A

NAPIT *Dangerous Situations Report*

For reporting an observed dangerous situation. Please complete all the unshaded areas.

NAPIT

Original for the owner / occupier
Copy required by electrician and 3rd party (if required)

NA/DS

Page | of

Address of installation		Date	
		Postcode	
Inspector	Member No.	Signature	

To the owner/occupier: A dangerous situation has been observed. It is recommended that it is made safe until remedial works can be undertaken. Details of the dangerous situation are recorded below.

Defect details

© Copyright NAPIT January 2018

I have been informed of this dangerous situation | Yes | No

I give my permission to make the dangerous situation safe | Yes | No

(In not agreeing to make safe I understand that I take responsibility)

Owner/occupier | Signature

NAPIT 4th Floor, Mill 3, Pleasley Vale Business Park, Mansfield, Nottinghamshire NG19 8RL

NA/DS/001 (V5)

Appendix 2

Verification, Inspection and Testing information sheets

Verification, Inspection and Testing information sheets

Domestic installations: 12 Easy steps to Safe Isolation

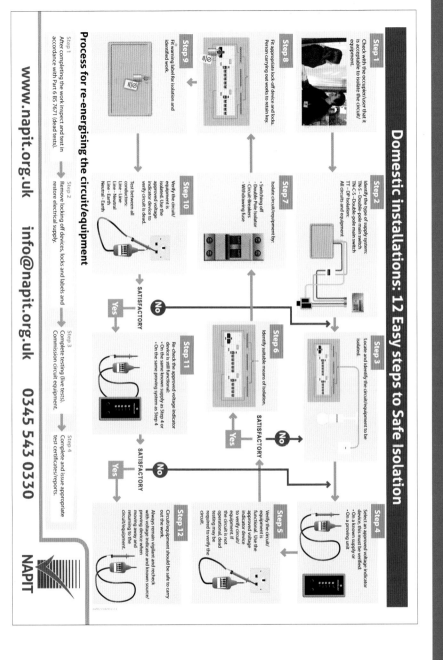

Step 1
Check with the occupier/user that it is acceptable to isolate the circuit/equipment.

Step 2
Identify the type of supply system:
TN-S - Double-pole main switch
TN-C-S - Double-pole main switch
TT - DP Isolation:
All circuits and equipment

Step 3
Locate and identify the circuit/equipment to be isolated.

Step 4
Select an approved voltage indicator device, this must be verified:
• On a known supply or
• On a proving unit

Step 5
Verify the circuit/equipment is functional. Use the approved voltage indicator device to verify the circuit/equipment. If the circuit is not operational, dead testing may be required to verify the circuit.

SATISFACTORY — No

Step 6
Identify suitable means of isolation.

SATISFACTORY — No / Yes

Step 7
Isolate circuit/equipment by:
• Switching off
• Double Pole isolator
• Circuit-breakers
• Withdrawing fuse

Step 8
Fit appropriate lock off device and locks. Person carrying out works to retain key.

Step 9
Fit warning label for isolation and identified work.

Step 10
Verify the circuit/equipment is isolated. Use the approved voltage indicator device to verify circuit is dead.
Test between all conductors:
Line - Line
Line - Neutral
Line - Earth
Neutral - Earth

SATISFACTORY — No / Yes

Step 11
Re-check the approved voltage indicator device is still functional:
• On a known supply as Step 4 or
• On the same proving system as Step 4

SATISFACTORY — No / Yes

Step 12
Circuit/equipment should be safe to carry out the work.
Always remain vigilant and recheck with voltage indicator and known source/proving device when moving away and returning to the circuit/equipment.

Process for re-energising the circuit/equipment

Step 1
After completing the work inspect and test in accordance with Part 6 BS 7671 (dead tests).

Step 2
Remove locking off devices, locks and labels and restore electrical supply.

Step 3
Complete testing (live tests). Commission circuit equipment.

Step 4
Complete and issue appropriate test certificates/reports.

www.napit.org.uk   info@napit.org.uk   0345 543 0330   NAPIT

Verification, Inspection and Testing information sheets

Industrial and Commercial installations: 12 Easy steps to Safe Isolation

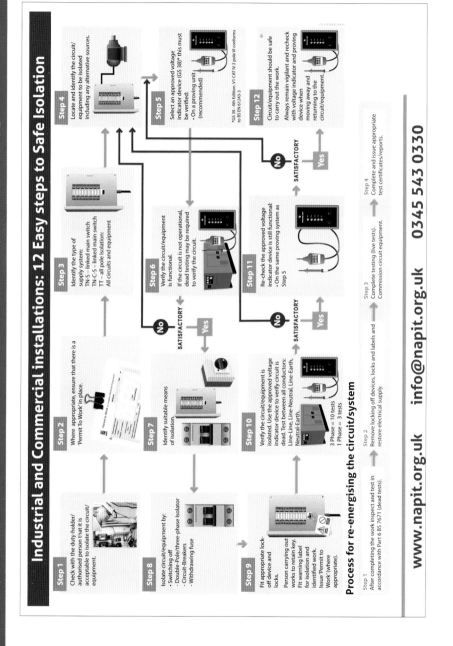

Step 1
Check with the duty-holder/authorised person that it is acceptable to isolate the circuit/equipment.

Step 2
Where appropriate, ensure that there is a 'Permit To Work' in place.

Step 3
Identify the type of supply system:
TN-S – linked main switch
TN-C-S – linked main switch
TT – all pole Isolation:
All circuits and equipment

Step 4
Locate and identify the circuit/equipment to be isolated including any alternative sources.

Step 5
Select an approved voltage indicator device (GS 38* this must be verified:
· On a proving unit (recommended)

*GS 38 - 4th Edition. VI CAT IV 2 pole VI conforms to BS EN 61243-3

Step 6
Verify the circuit/equipment is functional.
If the circuit is not operational, dead testing may be required to verify the circuit.

Step 7
Identify suitable means of isolation.

Step 8
Isolate circuit/equipment by:
· Switching off
· Double-Pole/three-phase Isolator
· Circuit-Breakers
· Withdrawing fuse

Step 9
Fit appropriate lock-off device and locks.
Person carrying out works to retain key.
Fit warning label for isolation and identified work.
Issue 'Permit to Work' (where appropriate).

Step 10
Verify the circuit/equipment is isolated. Use the approved voltage indicator device to verify circuit is dead. Test between all conductors;
Line-Line, Line-Neutral, Line-Earth, Neutral-Earth.

3 Phase = 10 tests
1 Phase = 3 tests

Step 11
Re-check the approved voltage indicator device is still functional:
· On the same proving system as Step 5

Step 12
Circuit/equipment should be safe to carry out the work.
Always remain vigilant and recheck with voltage indicator and proving device when moving away and returning to the circuit/equipment.

SATISFACTORY — No / Yes

Process for re-energising the circuit/system

Step 1
After completing the work inspect and test in accordance with Part 6 BS 7671 (dead tests).

Step 2
Remove locking off devices, locks and labels and restore electrical supply.

Step 3
Complete testing (live tests).
Commission circuit equipment.

Step 4
Complete and issue appropriate test certificates/reports.

www.napit.org.uk   info@napit.org.uk   0345 543 0330

MAXIMUM MEASURED EARTH FAULT LOOP IMPEDANCE
[Zs] (TN Systems) 18th Edition 2018 at 80% of Tables 41.2, 41.3 and 41.4

P/Device Rating AMPS	BS 88-2 (E bolt & G clip)		BS 88-3 (Fuse Sys. C)		BS 3036 (Fuse)		BS 1361/2 (Fuse) (BS 1362 Plug Top)		BS 3871 TYPE 1	BS 3871 TYPE 2	BS 3871 TYPE 3	BS EN 60898 / BS 61009-1 B (*D 5 Sec.)	BS EN 60898 / BS 61009-1 C (*D 5 Sec.)	BS EN 60898 / BS 61009-1 D (*D 5 Sec.)
	0.4 s	5 s	0.4 s	5 s	0.4 s	5 s	0.4 s	5 s	0.4/5 s	0.4/5 s	0.4/5 s	0.4/5 s	0.4/5 s	0.4 s
2	26.5	35.2	N/A	N/A	N/A	N/A	N/A	N/A	N/A	N/A	N/A	N/A	N/A	N/A
3	N/A	N/A	N/A	N/A	N/A	N/A	12.48	17.60	N/A	N/A	N/A	11.66	N/A	N/A
4	12.5	16.8	N/A	N/A	N/A	N/A	N/A	N/A	N/A	N/A	N/A	N/A	N/A	N/A
5	N/A	N/A	7.94	11.68	7.28	13.44	7.94	12.44	8.74	4.99	3.50	N/A	N/A	N/A
6	6.24	9.60	N/A	N/A	N/A	N/A	N/A	N/A	7.22	4.08	2.91	5.82	2.91	1.45
10	3.72	5.44	N/A	N/A	N/A	N/A	N/A	N/A	4.37	2.50	1.75	3.49	1.75	0.87
13	N/A	N/A	N/A	N/A	N/A	N/A	1.83	2.90	N/A	N/A	N/A	N/A	N/A	N/A
15	N/A	N/A	N/A	N/A	1.94	4.06	2.48	3.8	2.85	1.66	1.16	N/A	N/A	N/A
16	1.94	3.20	1.84	3.12	N/A	N/A	N/A	N/A	2.66	1.56	1.09	2.18	1.09	0.54
20	1.34	2.24	1.54	2.56	1.34	2.91	1.29	2.13	2.18	1.25	0.87	1.75	0.87	0.44
25	1.03	1.76	N/A	N/A	N/A	N/A	N/A	N/A	1.75	1.00	0.70	1.39	0.69	0.35
30	N/A	N/A	N/A	N/A	0.83	2.00	0.87	1.39	1.46	0.83	0.58	N/A	N/A	N/A
32	0.79	1.36	0.73	1.28	N/A	N/A	N/A	N/A	1.37	0.78	0.55	1.10	0.54	0.27
40	0.60	1.04	N/A	N/A	N/A	N/A	N/A	N/A	1.09	0.62	0.44	0.87	0.44	0.22
45	NA	N/A	0.46	0.80	0.45	1.20	N/A	0.72	0.97	0.55	0.39	0.77	0.38	0.19
50	0.46	0.79	N/A	N/A	N/A	N/A	N/A	N/A	0.87	0.50	0.35	0.69	0.35	0.17
60	N/A	N/A	N/A	N/A	0.32	0.86	N/A	0.53	N/A	N/A	N/A	N/A	N/A	N/A
63	0.35	0.62	0.29	0.54	N/A	N/A	N/A	N/A	0.69	0.40	0.28	0.55	0.28	0.13
80	N/A	0.44	N/A	0.41	N/A	N/A	N/A	0.38	0.55	0.31	0.22	0.43	0.22	0.10
100	N/A	0.34	N/A	0.30	N/A	0.40	N/A	0.26	0.44	0.25	0.17	0.31	0.17	0.07
125	N/A	0.26	N/A	N/A	N/A	N/A	N/A	N/A	N/A	N/A	N/A	0.27	0.13	0.06
160	N/A	0.21	N/A	N/A	N/A	N/A	N/A	N/A	N/A	N/A	N/A	N/A	N/A	N/A
200	N/A	0.14	N/A	N/A	N/A	N/A	N/A	N/A	N/A	N/A	N/A	N/A	N/A	N/A
250	N/A	N/A	N/A	N/A	N/A	N/A	N/A	N/A	N/A	N/A	N/A	N/A	N/A	N/A

*For BS EN 60898 / 61009 Type 'D' 5 Sec. Please use Type 'C' Column.
NAPIT Group 2018 (2 Document No NA/TDZD2b V4)

www.napit.org.uk   0345 543 0330

NAPIT

Information sheet

Table 7.1 (ii) Installation reference methods and cable ratings for 70 °C Thermoplastic (PVC) insulated and sheathed flat cable with protective conductor

Ref. Description	Installation reference method	Conductor cross-sectional area (mm2)						
		1.0 mm²	1.5 mm²	2.5 mm²	4 mm²	6 mm²	10 mm²	16 mm²
A	Enclosed in conduit in an insulated wall	11.5A	14.5A	20A	26A	32A	44A	57A
B*	Enclosed in conduit or trunking on a wall etc,	13A	16.5A	23A	30A	38A	52A	69A
C	Clipped direct	16A	20A	27A	37A	47A	64A	85A
100	In contact with the plasterboard ceiling or joists covered by thermal insulation not exceeding 100 mm	13A	16A	21A	27A	34A	45A	57A
101	In contact with plasterboard ceiling or joists covered by thermal insulation exceeding 100mm	10.5A	13A	17A	22A	27A	36A	46A
102	In the stud wall with thermal insulation with cable touching the wall	13A	16A	21A	27A	35A	47A	63A
103	Surrounded by thermal insulation including in a stud wall with thermal insulation with cable not touching a wall	8A	10A	13.5A	17.5A	23.5A	32A	42.5A

Notes :
1. Cable ratings taken from Table 4D5 of BS 7671
2. B* taken from Table 4D2A of BS7671, see Appendix F.

NA/MME/1120/v5)

www.napit.org.uk   0345 543 0330

NAPIT

Bespoke insurance

Designed with NAPIT members in mind.

Members have access to:
- Tailored cover specific to their line of work
- Specialist advice from people who understand NAPIT members' needs
- Comprehensive cover including professional indemnity, public liability, inefficacy
- Relevant options including personal accident insurance
- Practical considerations including life insurance, critical illness cover and income protection
- Essential health and safety advice through our partner Stallard Kane

Get in touch!

We're not a call centre – our team of professional advisers are available to discuss your current insurance programme or answer any insurance related questions you may have.

Enquire today: **0330 9000 701** or visit
www.napitinsurance.co.uk

info@napitinsurance.co.uk